KU-566-652

BAIRD OF TELEVISION

JOHN LOGIE BAIRD.

BAIRD OF TELEVISION

THE LIFE STORY OF JOHN LOGIE BAIRD

By RONALD F. TILTMAN
Author of
"Television for the Home"
"Wireless Without Worry"
&c. &c.

With a Foreword by
Lord ANGUS KENNEDY
Vice-President of the Television Society

WITH MANY ILLUSTRATIONS

LONDON
Seeley Service & Co
Limited

1934(?)

PRINTED IN GREAT BRITAIN

TO

DIANA BAIRD

AND

JANET TILTMAN

Both you young women were born in 1932, *and so you come in at the dawn of the wonderful new era which television opens up before us. Already the television receiver is in tens of thousands of homes, and by the time you have grown up sufficiently to read this volume it will be a commonplace feature of home-life which you will accept as calmly as your electric light and telephone. You will certainly pity your fathers' primitive existence when you learn that there was a time when they could not see the person at the other end of the telphone line, when they could not watch the artistes in the broadcasting studios, and when they waited to read reports on events of national importance in the Press instead of viewing them instantaneously on a home screen.*

You will be fortunate indeed to have at your command a power to equal the potentialities of the fabled Magic Carpet, a machine which will show you scenes of far-off lands in colour and stereoscopic relief. In past years your fathers have sat at home and criticised the quality of the voices broadcast, but you will have the additional privilege of grumbling at the features and costumes seen—you may even address an indignant letter to the Press protesting against the announcer who will wear a soft collar and spats!

It needs but little imagination to visualise the marvellous vistas television opens to you, so I hope you will both, in due course, appreciate in its true worth the inspiring story of the birth of this science and of the man who liberated it from Nature's womb.

The day will come when you, Diana, will be proud of your surname!

FOREWORD

BY

LORD ANGUS KENNEDY
Vice-President, Television Society

NEVER since the days when King Robert Bruce, inspired by the example of a spider, freed his country from an oppressor, has Scotland produced a more romantic hero than John Logie Baird, the man who made his wildest dreams come true, and, successfully combating ill-health and poverty, by dogged perseverance achieved what nearly every one regarded as the impossible.

Born and brought up in a Scottish manse, his inventive genius showed itself at an early age; but the world is all too sceptical of young inventors and, after some good technical experience, he went South, like many another Scot, to seek his fortune in the world of commerce. A breakdown in health ultimately led to the fulfilment of his dreams, and the coming into the world of television; but the path was thorny and led through extreme privations and the proverbial attic.

Great as was his genius, even greater was the courage with which he overcame each new difficulty as it arose. He has the Celtic imagination with the gift of turning fantasies into facts. Someone once said to me: "Baird talks more nonsense than anyone I ever met, but in time his nonsense always becomes sense."

When his invention was at quite an early stage many of his friends regarded his statement that the Derby would soon be seen by television as rash; but as, in 1932, a thousand people witnessed the finish of that great race from a cinema near Victoria Station, his prophecy was fulfilled.

Baird is no boaster, having the shyness and modesty which so frequently accompany greatness, combined with a certain genuineness and charm. He has a deep understanding of life, gained from experience rather than theory, while his generosity will probably prevent his ever becoming rich.

What the ultimate development of television will lead to, it is impossible to say. I for one believe that it will be of great value in linking up the Empire, and that the name of Baird will go down to posterity as a pioneer of civilisation who enabled one continent to see another.

If there are any who think that life is easy for such pioneers they will certainly be disillusioned by Mr. Tiltman's excellent biography, which will be of supreme interest to all, faithfully chronicling, as it does, the history of a man of great personality who set himself out to probe the mysteries of the ether, who struggled and attained, learning to regard both disaster and triumph with equanimity, who has become a world-famous inventor, and is, like ourselves, a human being. I add this advisedly, knowing there are still some who regard his achievement of "seeing at a distance" as savouring more of magic than of honest toil!

Perhaps this work will enlighten them.

ANGUS KENNEDY.

PREFACE

> "*Talent is that which is in a man's power:*
> *Genius is that in whose power a man is.*"
>
> LOWELL.

I MAKE no apology, nor, indeed, is one called for, in setting down on permanent record the romantic life-story of John Logie Baird, the Scottish engineer who in the past eight years has found himself raised from the obscurity of an attic to world fame.

The name of Baird is as indissolubly linked for all time with television as that of Marconi with wireless.

No branch of scientific research in recent years has excited greater public interest than television, which gives us vision over any wired or wireless electrical circuit and enables us to see through brick walls, from town to town, from country to country.

In England, Germany, France, and Italy the Baird television system is being actively developed and occupies a supreme position, while in Britain short television transmissions are practically a daily feature of the the British Broadcasting Corporation's programmes. During the past year or two in this country we have had opportunity in our homes of watching broadcast demonstrations of golf, cricket and tennis strokes, ju-jutsu and boxing, while the gradual development of this new form of home entertainment has enabled us to view cartoonists at work, conjurers, jugglers, dancers, ventriloquists, marionettes, and short plays, and it is now estimated that there are something like ten thousand to twelve thousand British enthusiasts equipped with television receivers.

Science has been harnessed for so many different purposes recently that we are apt to accept these wonders without troubling to consider the romantic stories of their discoveries, yet the field of technical research has its victories no less decisive than the field of battle and the laboratory has its romances—and surely the story of John Logie Baird is both a romance and a victory which will ensure for him an enduring place in scientific history.

Many important discoveries in this world have been made by amateur investigators working quite alone, unaided by either technical or financial assistance, and television is no exception in this respect.

From the very first, Baird had no expert assistance whatever, and although hampered continually by ill-health and lack of funds, he laboured patiently at his stupendous task of conquering television unaided. Considering that in many countries scientists had worked fruitlessly in well-equipped laboratories for years, this was a one-man job in which nothing less than a genius could hope to succeed.

In his attic, alone, with home-made apparatus of most primitive type, Baird solved what had proved to be one of the most difficult scientific problems of recent times and proved his genius!

I use the term genius deliberately, for my Webster's *New International Dictionary* defines the word thus: "Extraordinary mental superiority; uncommon native intellectual powers; highly unusual power of invention or origination of any kind." I am convinced that after reading the story of Baird's life and achievements, which I am now privileged to give in its entirety to the world, nobody will challenge this term.

Baird was the first man in the world to achieve television, the first man to commercialise television. He placed British television in the van of world progress and, in my opinion, has maintained its pre-eminent position up till now. Who will deny this pioneer the status which is his by right of his accomplishments?

I must place on record my appreciation of the assistance I have received in the preparation of this biography of one for whose personality I have great admiration and for whose achievements a profound respect.

Miss Annie Baird, of Helensburgh, the inventor's sister, was good enough to let me have most useful notes on her brother's boyhood, and Mr. G. Fullerton Robertson, a lifelong friend of Baird's, supplied me with much information of a most intimate and valuable character.

Finally, I have to thank Mr. Baird himself for his courtesy in placing at my disposal information otherwise unobtainable, for giving me access to records and documents not available to any other writer, and for permission to reproduce most of the illustrations in this volume. He was good enough to read through the manuscript and thus verify the basic facts, but the opinions expressed on, and the conclusions drawn from, these facts are, of course, mine entirely.

RONALD F. TILTMAN.

LIST OF CONTENTS

LIST OF ILLUSTRATIONS

LIST OF ILLUSTRATIONS

CHAPTER ONE

"A SON OF THE MANSE"

CHAPTER ONE

"A SON OF THE MANSE"

SITUATED at the mouth of the lovely Gareloch stands Helensburgh, Dumbartonshire, once a quiet fishing village, but now a flourishing watering place and termed the Madeira of Scotland. While Helensburgh itself has gradually developed to its present popularity, one part of it remains practically unchanged to this day. This is "The Lodge," Argyle Street, a venerable grey sandstone house set in the midst of an old-world garden, and it was at this house that John Logie Baird first saw the light of day at 8 a.m. on 13th August 1888.

His father was the minister of the West Parish Church, and was known and respected throughout South-west Scotland for his scholarly attainments and genial disposition, and it is interesting to note that the Rev. John Baird, now over ninety years of age, still resides at the house where his illustrious son was born.

John Logie was the youngest of four; his elder sister now cares for her old father at Helensburgh; a younger sister, Jean, married the Rev. Neil Conley;

and an elder brother, James, is now farming in Australia. His mother, Jessie Morrison Inglis, was one of the famous Inglis family, prominent shipbuilders in Glasgow, and it is from this side of the ancestry that he probably inherits his scientific bias. Mrs. Baird died in 1924, thus she did not live to see her son world famous. His father comes from a long line of farmers, the Bairds of Falkirk being well known and respected in that district.

From his earliest childhood Baird was extremely delicate, and at one time was not expected to live to maturity. He seems, however, to have had a certain tenacity, and in spite of his very poor state of health was an extremely active youngster. During his earliest boyhood days he displayed to a marked extent the constructive and pioneering instinct which was later in life to bring him world fame.

At the age of six years Baird went to a local school with his sisters, later transferring to a boys' school before entering Larchfield Academy at the age of ten. He was not a brilliant scholar by any means, bad health being a great handicap. In spite of a delicate constitution he quickly established himself as the leader of the youth of the village.

"The Lodge" soon became a hive of engineering activity, and young Baird's first experimental work may be said to be connected with the telephone, for with the aid of youthful friends he rigged up a circuit consisting of the conventional two biscuit tins connected with string. This did not long satisfy Baird, so his next step was to fix up an improved circuit from wire nails bound round with wire, two tins and an electric battery. Later this developed into a more elaborate telephone exchange in his bedroom with wires slung precariously across several neighbouring streets to link up his home with that of four school friends, any one of whom could be switched through to the other by the young experimenter.

One stormy night, however, a telephone wire blew down across the road in a gale and a luckless local cabman was caught under the chin and lifted off his seat. Under the natural impression that the newly formed National Telephone Company was to blame, the driver demanded damages, and the company's officials found that an unauthorised rival was in the field, for it was "that boy Baird's" wire. Immediate steps were taken to suppress the modest telephone system, and it may be said that here for the first time Baird ran against large vested interests of the type which he had to face later in life.

The historic little telephone exchange is still preserved in Baird's room at "The Lodge," and beside the plugs can be seen the battered name-plates bearing the names of his four old school-mates who were linked by the system—Whimster, Bruce, Norwell, and Wadsworth. The latter to-day holds an important position in a prominent London accountancy firm.

As a schoolboy Baird was greatly interested in electricity, and following the abrupt conclusion of the telephone system, his next activity was to install an electric light plant single-handed at the old manse. The current was generated by a home-made dynamo, driven by a water-wheel worked from the water main and a symposium of accumu-lators made out of old jam jars and sheet lead.

In a recent letter to me Miss Annie Baird quite correctly pointed out that they could claim to be the first family in Helensburgh to have their own electric light plant and private telephone system!

Apart from a keen interest in electricity Baird displayed a natural aptitude for engineering and mechanical devices during his schooldays. He pur-chased an ancient and dilapidated tri-car for £4, 10*s.* and this was patched up with the aid of friends and rushed through the streets of the borough to the great annoyance of the neighbours, who christened the antiquated automobile "Young Baird's Reaper and Binder," owing to the appalling noise made by its rattling chains and ramshackle mechanism. This car was not a good economic project, as it so frequently had to be pushed home, but it provided plenty of excitement for Baird and his young companions.

It is interesting to note that Baird's closest friend in his early schooldays was Jack Buchanan, now the famous star of the theatrical world. Buchanan lived close to the Manse, and the two boys were frequently in each other's houses. Miss Annie Baird recalls the time the two boys spent together and has given me instances of the difference in their character. She remembers Jack Buchanan as a very neat and tidy boy, always well dressed and extremely fond of music, while John Baird was carelessly dressed, had perpetually ruffled hair, seemed to "keep his mind in the clouds," and invariably looked "as if he had been drawn through a hedge backwards."

Baird has a fund of stories to tell of his association with Jack Buchanan in their schooldays.

Both boys were very keen on photography, and a photographic club was formed in the village with Baird as President and Buchanan as the leading spirit. Incidentally, here again Baird showed his pioneer spirit by going further into the subject than any of the other boys; he enlarged photographs first through a hole in the window shutter and then by means of an old magic lantern, and he experimented with flash-light and by delayed exposure photographed himself in bed asleep.

However, the subject of photography became dreary in time to the bulk of the members and they became restive and created disturbances. To reduce the meeting to order a by-law was passed that any member of the club creating a disturbance should be bent over and receive one stroke of the cane from each of the other members. This proved a much more exciting diversion than the discussion of photography, and soon the club had changed into a centre for castigation and became famous as the "One All Round Club." At each meeting various offences were reviewed and dealt with summarily.

The eagerness for castigation displayed by some of the more muscular members of the club caused wholesale resignations on the part of the less muscular ones; then a second by-law imposed a penalty of five shillings and "six all round" for any member who tendered his resignation.

This club did not confine its activities to castigation and photography, but any outsider who offended a member of the club was liable to draw down upon himself the revenge of the united

BAIRD'S ELECTRIC LIGHT PLANT.

BAIRD WAS KEENLY INTERESTED IN ELECTRICITY & ENGINEERING IN HIS SCHOOLDAYS & IS SEEN HERE WITH HIS HOME-MADE PLANT WITH WHICH HE SUPPLIED "THE LODGE" WITH ELECTRIC LIGHT.

CELEBRITIES IN EARLY DAYS.

THE ARGYLE STREET CRICKET CLUB, HELENSBURGH. BAIRD IS ON LEFT OF BACK ROW WHILE ON RIGHT OF FRONT ROW IS HIS BOYHOOD FRIEND JACK BUCHANAN, THE WELL-KNOWN ACTOR.

members. On one occasion an elderly and respectable resident of Helensburgh had offended Jack Buchanan by—if Baird's memory serves correctly—boxing his ears. This unspeakable outrage upon the club's leading member was punished by the members assembling one night, creeping through the offender's garden, directing a ladder against his pigeon-house and removing all the pigeons and wringing their necks. Baird tells me that even after all these years he can still recall how, trembling in every limb, he held a ladder while Jack Buchanan climbed to the pigeon-house.

At the age of about seventeen or eighteen Baird entered the Royal Technical College, Glasgow, to follow the course for electrical engineering. Among his fellow-students at this time was J. C. W. Reith, also a son of the manse, who is now Sir John Reith, the forceful Director-General of the British Broadcasting Corporation. Baird passed through the course with some distinction and was awarded the Diploma and Associateship of the College in this subject. His father did not approve of his choice at the time and wanted John to enter the Church. Baird sometimes thinks, in the midst of his strenuous life, that it would have meant a far more peaceful career if he had followed his father's advice!

After taking his Associateship he went to Glasgow University, where he spent most of his time studying Electrical Engineering and Pure Physics, subjects in which he did fairly well, but did not distinguish himself. At this time Baird brought out an invention for dispensing with the commutator on the direct current motor. He studied for the B.Sc. degree and went through the complete curriculum, being in the final year when war broke out. It was his intention to return later to put in the few months' residence necessary to complete the course, but subsequent events prevented this.

Actually he never entered Glasgow University again until, many years later, he delivered a lecture on his then famous television system to a gathering of eminent professors in the engineering classroom.

Baird had also served his apprenticeship as an engineer in the shops of Haley's Industrial Motors and the Argyle Motor Works. Apprentice engineers in Scotland in those days led a hard life. The shops opened at 5.30 a.m., and as overtime was the rule rather than the exception, he was away from home from before daylight till late at night. These long hours meant that the disturbing smells and noises which had issued from the Manse in the course of his experiments came to a rather gratifying end.

During the time Baird was attending the College and University he carried out a good deal of experimental work in connection with electricity and the construction of selenium cells. This was, however, not carried on in the University laboratories, as the regular curriculum precluded original experiments being undertaken. The kitchen at "The Lodge" was rather the scene of his early research efforts and he spent a good deal of time here with selenium cells in an endeavour to devise a satisfactory talking film and also in some very early attempts to solve the problems of television—the latter in those days being regarded as merely the dream of the imaginative novelist. The kitchen experiments did not lead to any practical results whatever, but they certainly gave rise to many only too well-founded complaints of disagreeable smells due to the burning of selenium.

The full story of Baird's early days is of importance for four quite definite reasons.

Firstly, because it shows us so clearly how from the very start of life he had to battle with the continual handicap of poor health and a frail physique, and how by sheer determination of will he overcame this handicap sufficiently to take a leading part in the juvenile activities of his village.

Secondly, it shows us just how early in life Baird's

inventive, pioneering and constructive instincts manifested themselves in unmistakable form.

Thirdly, because we note how his earliest original research work was carried on, not in the well-equipped laboratories of a university, but in the most primitive manner on a kitchen table—experience of great value to him in after years when working on a problem of great magnitude with the most primitive equipment and restricted accommodation.

Finally, because we see how his first situation as an engineering apprentice helped him to develop that amazing capacity for hard work throughout a long day—a capacity that was to prove invaluable to him in after years during his prolonged one-man experiments when wrestling with the secret of television!

C H A P T E R   T W O

BUSINESS ACTIVITIES

CHAPTER TWO

BUSINESS ACTIVITIES

THE outbreak of the Great War interrupting his course at Glasgow University, Baird immediately offered himself for enlistment, but was rejected on the grounds of physical unfitness. He then took the position as Superintendent Engineer with the Clyde Valley Electrical Power Company, this being the Company which supplied electricity to the great shipbuilding yards and engineering and munition works which lined the banks of the Clyde, and held that position throughout the war period.

His work as Superintendent Engineer entailed continual attention, involving being out all hours of the day and night to superintend the repair of breakdowns in the distribution plant, and Baird's health, which, as the earlier chapter shows, was poor, suffered very severely under the strain imposed by these conditions. He just held out until the conclusion of hostilities, but at the end of the War he determined to abandon engineering altogether, feeling that it would be quite impossible for him to make any advance in this career, as he had not the physique or constitution to cope successfully with the strenuous life involved.

Coming of a family whose circumstances at that time were not exactly affluent, when Baird gave up his engineering career he found himself with the proverbial £10 in his pocket, and he boldly determined to start in business for himself with a patent sock he had invented. This was "The Baird Undersock," to be worn under the ordinary sock. It was medicated and self-absorbent, prevented the dye from socks passing to the feet, and was guaranteed to keep the feet cool in summer and warm in winter.

Baird prepared these socks himself in a little attic office, and his first venture into the realms of salesmanship consisted of carrying six dozen of these socks and selling them to retail chemists round about Glasgow. They proved a great success in Glasgow and were widely sold by the leading chemists and stores. Encouraged by this success Baird brought out a special shoe cleaner, the "Osmo Boot Polish," and within a year this young Scotsman had built up a prosperous little business and began to make money at a fairly rapid rate—a success well deserved.

Unfortunately Baird's old bogey, ill-health, re-

AN ELECTRICAL ENGINEERING CAREER.

BEING UNFIT FOR MILITARY SERVICE BAIRD HELD THE POSITION OF SUPERINTENDENT ENGINEER WITH THE CLYDE VALLEY ELECTRICAL POWER CO. THROUGHOUT THE WAR. HE IS SEEN IN THE RUTHEGLEN SUB-STATION IN 1915.

FROM ELECTRICITY TO JAM MAKING!

A UNIQUE PHOTOGRAPH OF BAIRD'S PRIMITIVE "JAM FACTORY" WHICH HE ESTABLISHED IN THE HEART OF THE JUNGLE ON THE ISLAND OF TRINIDAD.

turned and his health gave way again under the strain and worry of commercial life. He sold the growing business to a well-known Glasgow merchant, liquidated all available assets and determined to risk everything in the pursuit of health.

After reading in guide-books and pamphlets the most glowing accounts of the climate and scenic charms of the West Indies, and in particular the Island of Trinidad, he secured a number of agencies and sailed for Trinidad with a view to supplying goods to the natives of that region.

Arriving at Port of Spain, the capital of the Island, with his trunk-load of samples of cotton goods and fancy articles, Baird found that the selling of goods to the natives was a decidedly over-crowded profession—to put it mildly. In Baird's own words: "The whole Port of Spain appeared to be populated entirely by commission agents, and the commission agents' chief source of income appeared to be borrowing from new-comers."

Realising that the commission business was of no use to him, Baird disposed of his samples and looked around enterprisingly to find some other form of profitable undertaking without delay. It soon struck him that there should be room for the development of a jam and preserves industry, for much of the fruit that grew in such profusion on the island was left to rot on the ground, since the fruit steamers did not call at the island at that time. Trinidad was also, of course, one of the principal sugar-growing centres of the West Indies, so that the ingredients for jam-making were available locally in abundance.

Having surveyed the island, Baird decided to establish his new undertaking in the fruit-growing district of the Santa Cruz Valley, some sixteen miles away from the capital. The village chosen was named Bourgmullatrice, meaning "The City of the Black Man," although its inhabitants were every colour under the sun—except white. Here Baird, the only white man in the village at that time, made his primitive factory arrangements, comprising three bamboo huts and the erection of large copper vats to be heated by wood fires for jam-boiling purposes.

The very first boiling attempted was hardly so successful as might be desired, for as the fragrant odour of the stewing fruit and sugar was wafted down the Santa Cruz Valley it brought myriads of insects out of the surrounding jungle, and these flew straight into the vats of boiling jam! It was mass hari-kari. However, with patience and ingenuity, two of the qualities this Scotsman has demonstrated throughout his career, the many difficulties were overcome one by one and the jam industry was being gradually developed.

Here, once again, Baird's physique was against him, and after about a year the unhealthy conditions under which he was living brought on a severe bout of malaria fever. Believing that the preserving enterprise could be developed on more ambitious lines by the establishment of an export trade to Great Britain, Baird decided to seek health in England once more and, leaving a friend in charge in Trinidad, he came back to London and opened a small office in Pimlico to handle the jam business at that end. However, the Trinidad climate proved equally unattractive to his friend, the industry was abandoned, and the wattle hut "factory" sold for £5 to another friend who wished to establish a mat-making industry on the island.

Thus the year 1920 found him back in London with no occupation, quite limited funds saved from the West Indian activities, and without any improvement in his poor state of health. Once again he had to apply his fertile brain to the question of taking up some form of business to support himself.

I was very interested to hear from Miss Annie Baird that her brother stayed with her in London for about six weeks during this year, the first occasion that they had met for a few years. Throughout his varied commercial ventures Baird had never forgotten his favourite hobby, which was scientific research, and at this time he was strongly inclined to abandon commerce and take up scientific research work. He had two ideas in his mind at the time, apparently, and could not decide whether to work on the problem of a razor blade that would not blunt or to take up the thread of his television experiments where he had left off some years before in the kitchen of his Helensburgh home.

He asked his sister for advice several times, and she, quite wisely as it appeared at the time, strongly advised him to take up the razor blade problem and to leave television alone. But, Miss Baird tells me, "he evidently did not take my advice!"

However, he put thoughts of scientific work aside for a while and again entered the commercial world for a livelihood, this time dealing in Australian honey. He noticed that this, at the time, was obtainable in the market at the absurdly low figure of 18*s.* to 21*s.* a cwt., and boldly invested the whole of his modest capital in the commodity. He packed it in small tins, advertised it attractively, and disposed of it at nearly double the cost. Thanks to the untiring energy again displayed by Baird this honey business turned out very profitable and within a matter of six months or so he had sufficient capital behind him to purchase a half-share in a small business dealing in coir fibre dust. This dust is extracted from coco-nuts in the process of manufacturing matting, and is valuable as a fertiliser for horticultural purposes. This business also was profitable, and then once again came the old story—another breakdown in health and orders to take a complete rest. Selling his share of the business he went to the Buxton Hydro seeking health and strength.

The latter part of 1921 found Baird back in London once again with a rapidly dwindling capital, but improved health and courage as stout as ever. This time his versatile ability was directed into a new channel and he took up the soap business. He purchased the soap from a small manufacturer, who boiled it in some mews on the outskirts of London; it was neatly wrapped as Baird's "Speedy Cleaner" in 1lb. twin tablets, and then sold very cheaply through travellers calling on back-street grocers and the smaller retail shops.

The prosperity of this business necessitated the importation of large quantities of soap from France and Belgium to augment the London supply, and a small company was formed to develop the business still further. It seemed at last that Baird was to reap the benefit of his dogged commercial ability and perseverance, that fortune might turn a smiling face in his direction.

Unfortunately (or fortunately as subsequent events proved) this was the time when Baird had the most severe set-back of all. He had a complete physical and nervous breakdown of a serious character, and after a thorough examination his doctor informed him that he must abandon for ever all thoughts of a business career in London.

He was ordered to take a prolonged and complete rest on the English south coast, and having chosen Hastings as a suitable resort he repaired there in the latter part of 1922 little better than a physical wreck. He had then no income whatever, and only his small capital saved from the soap business to support him.

It must have been in a very despondent frame of mind that Baird retired to Hastings, a young though broken man.

His activities in the commercial world form an amazing record of persistent enterprise and tenacity of will in the face of the vital handicap of ill-health, a record that one might go far to equal. Time and time again his unquenched pioneering spirit plunged him whole-heartedly into some new line of business, selected with the enterprise and developed with the forceful ability of the highest traditions of Scottish character. Time and time again fate intervened in the form of recurrent illness and swung back the pendulum of his career to the starting point once more.

Baird's earlier days were marked by the development of a strong creative impulse, the ability of a brilliant mind to triumph over physical imperfections, and the faculty of working hard and long under conditions of difficulty. His business essays show conclusively that these vital characteristics, which are becoming conspicuously absent in these days of the "dole," were forthcoming to an extraordinary extent during his amazingly diverse commercial activities.

Up to the time of his retirement to Hastings at the age of thirty-four, no one could accuse Baird of being favoured by fortune to the slightest extent; his modest business successes had been well deserved and his life to date had brought him far more difficulties, discomforts and disappointments than were merited.

Now the culminating blow of all was this breakdown, so utter and complete as momentarily to dim the spontaneous fire of an outstanding intellect.

Baird felt that he was broken—finished!

CHAPTER THREE

A MEMORABLE DECISION

CHAPTER THREE

A MEMORABLE DECISION

FOR the first few months in Hastings Baird's health was such that no activity of mind or body was possible, but gradually the fresh sea breezes and the healing powers of this famous watering-place began to take effect. With returning energy came the desire for activity once again.

Being debarred from the bustle of business life, and living the life of a recluse at that time, the work which came naturally to his mind was his old love—scientific research. In Chapter One is recorded how as a schoolboy Baird had dabbled with selenium cells in his kitchen experiments, and had even attempted to make a crude form of television apparatus. His mind reverting to the experiments of his schooldays, he took up once again his youthful hobby after a lapse of some ten years. He would make another and more determined attempt to achieve that fantastic dream—television!

Digression is here necessary in order to show in its true perspective the magnitude of the task which this convalescent young Scotsman had set himself.

The early history of the subject of television dates from the discovery of the light sensitive properties of selenium, an element the electrical resistance of which varies when light falls upon it. The discovery was made quite accidentally by a cable operator in Ireland in 1873, was communicated to the Society of Telegraph Engineers, and created widespread interest. Very soon selenium "cells" were constructed by Bell, Siemens, and others, and these appeared to open up immense possibilities. As these selenium cells provided a means of turning light into electricity, many research workers believed that the cells would give to the eye what the recently invented telephone had given to the ear and so make it possible to see by telegraphy.

Within a few years Senlee, Ayrton, and half a dozen other investigators had fully described systems which were to accomplish this spectacular feat, and it was predicted that in a short time it would be possible to obtain vision over an ordinary telephone line. However, it was soon proved that the capabilities of selenium to respond to the stupendous speed of signalling involved were greatly overrated, and while the telephone was steadily developed practical television remained at an absolute standstill.

Where the human eye could take in a whole

scene at a glance it was obviously impossible for a selenium cell to do this and many experimenters worked on the lines of using a separate cell for each point of the picture. Others used one cell only, using apparatus to cause each point of the picture to fall in rapid succession on it, the varying current from this cell to be transmitted to the receiving station where it would control a point of light traversing a screen exactly in step with the traversal of the image across the cell, the process to be carried out so rapidly that, owing to the persistence of vision, the eye would see not a succession of separate spots, but the whole moving image.

Speed was the essential thing in television, for the whole idea was to transmit the images of living scenes with such rapidity that they appeared instantaneous to the eye, with movements as smooth and natural as on the cinema screen.

Selenium had not been the only means of turning light into electricity available to the earlier television workers, for in 1888 Hertz and Hallwach made discoveries which led to the construction of what are known as photo-electric cells. These turn light into electricity and are instantaneous in their action. These new cells seemed to offer an advantageous substitute for the sluggish selenium and were a great stimulus to experimenters. Again disappointment, for the photo-electric cell proved insufficiently sensitive and would not respond to the very small light available. It was found that the human face, brilliantly illuminated by a powerful bank of lamps, reflected back light less than that of one candlepower.

Next came Fleming's invention of the thermionic valve, and its subsequent development into the three-electrode valve as used in radio to-day, and this seemed to alter the aspect of the problem, but even the great amplification obtained by use of the valve was insufficient to boost up the minute currents which could be directed upon the photo-electric cell for television purposes.

So the problem of television, so simple in theory, proved insurmountable in practice. For a full fifty years no appreciable progress was made towards a solution. Not that the subject was neglected. Throughout those fifty years many patient investigators had worked on the problem with a persistence that showed clearly the value they placed upon reaching their prized goal. Television proved itself to be one of the most difficult scientific problems of modern times, and after its long history of barren and unfruitful efforts it was quite reasonably predicted that anything from twenty to fifty further years would elapse before the living features of a person seated before a transmitter would be faithfully received and clearly recognised on a receiver.

That, briefly, was the position when John Logie Baird made his memorable decision at Hastings.

For fifty years the problem of television had defied solution in spite of vigorous attacks directed from every angle. Skilled professional research workers of various nationalities had wrestled with the complex problem—Baird was an amateur who had left his technical experience five years behind while building a business career. Many workers had approached the subject in the prime of their scientific career—Baird approached the subject as a young man struggling to recuperate from a complete breakdown of mind and body. Many workers had toiled at the problem in well-equipped laboratories—Baird had no laboratory, no equipment. Large sums of money had been spent in pursuit of a solution—Baird had but capital enough to ensure a roof over his head for a strictly limited period.

Romantic as are many of the pages of scientific history, was there ever more magnificent courage? Can one find the equal of this picture of a lion-hearted scientific Don Quixote setting forth to tilt at a windmill!

CHAPTER FOUR

IN A HASTINGS ATTIC

CHAPTER FOUR

IN A HASTINGS ATTIC

VISITORS to Hastings passing through an unpretentious passage-way close to the Town Hall see a bronze plaque attached to the partition wall of one of the small shops.

The inscription it bears is quite simple:

TELEVISION

FIRST DEMONSTRATED BY JOHN LOGIE BAIRD

FROM EXPERIMENTS STARTED HERE IN 1924

It was at No. 8 Queen's Arcade that Baird first commenced his serious attempt to solve the television problem. He occupied a small attic room over what was at the time a lock-up artificial-flower shop, although the premises have changed hands and trade since.

With the scanty funds at his disposal anything in the nature of a laboratory or laboratory equipment was entirely out of the question. However, while he was strictly limited in financial resources he was certainly unlimited in ingenuity.

In this little room the first crude experimental television apparatus was assembled on the wash-stand, which had to serve as a laboratory bench. Apparatus was almost too dignified a term to apply to the unpromising-looking collection of crude and makeshift objects.

An old tea-chest, purchased for a few coppers and carried through the Hastings streets, formed a base to carry the motor which rotated the exploring disc, while an empty biscuit box housed the projection lamp. Scanning discs were cut out of cardboard, and the mountings consisted of darning needles and old scrap timber. The necessary lenses on the optical side of the apparatus were procured from bicycle shops at a cost of fourpence each, while electric motors ready for the scrap-heap were pressed into service on duties for which they were never intended and were entirely unsuited.

As many wireless amateurs will remember, there was a great deal of ex-Government wireless apparatus to be picked up very cheaply about this time and nobody used more ingenuity than Baird in buying scraps of this apparatus and adapting it to his needs.

One or two old hat boxes were also utilised, and the whole conglomeration of bits and pieces was precariously held together with glue, sealing-wax and odd lengths of string. Over, under, and all around the apparatus ran an amazing tangle of wires—wires of all sizes, types, and colours, beside which a modern telephone exchange would look simple. A friend who called in this room shortly after the apparatus was collected together, told me that the general effect on entering reminded him of Heath Robinson at his best.

The question of current supply was not simple to arrange in view of the shortage of funds, for in these early experiments Baird found it necessary to employ very high voltages indeed at times. His necessary filament voltages were supplied from accumulators, but when it came to high tension supply he did what so many wireless amateurs did in early broadcasting days, he used rows of ordinary pocket flash-lamp batteries linked together with metal clips. These batteries gave a great deal of trouble at times and kept him busily employed in tracing faulty ones and substituting new flash-lamp batteries.

For months Baird laboured patiently in this attic endeavouring to persuade his nightmarish collection of apparatus to show some results. With the patience of the true research worker he attacked the problem from every angle, and when occasionally he ran against snags in branches of science where his knowledge or memory failed him, he browsed over technical books in the public library.

All the time, of course, his health was still in a very low state, and his funds were strictly limited—the only things he had in abundance were time, ingenuity, patience and courage!

In taking up the research work at Hastings, Baird felt that the *theory* of television appeared to

L share each CANADIAN PACIFIC RAILWAY COMMON STOCK in name of Akroyd and Smithers; transfer of the Stock has been stopped.—Apply to Parr and Rae, 10, Dale-street, Liverpool.

SEEING by WIRELESS.—Inventor of apparatus wishes to hear from someone who will assist (not financially) in making working model.—Write Box S.686, The Times, E.C.4.

MOTOR TOUR.—Gentleman, expert driver any car and European roads, wishes ACT CHAUFFEUR-COURIER fortnight tour; pay own expenses.—Write

This, Baird's first attempt to secure assistance when struggling with his makeshift apparatus at Hastings, produced no immediate result. It is an extract from *The Times* Personal column of 27th June 1923.

be quite simple. All the requirements seemed to be two optical exploring devices rotating in synchronisation, a light-sensitive cell of some sort, and a controlled light source, capable of extremely rapid variation, and all these appeared to be, to use a Patent Office term, already "known to the art." The problem of synchronisation appeared to have been practically solved in multiplex telegraphy; a number of optical exploring devices were known; the photo-electric cell in conjunction with the thermionic valve appeared to be a suitable light-sensitive device; and the glow discharge lamp seemed to be an ideal light source.

At the same time he realised that despite the apparent simplicity of the task the work of many men over many years had failed to bring this theory to practical accomplishment. He soon found that the main difficulty lay in the light-sensitive cell and concentrated all his attentions on that part of the system.

After months of unremitting work with his crude apparatus Baird's faith was at last rewarded in small measure, for one never-to-be-forgotten afternoon early in 1924 he got his various bits and pieces to hold together sufficiently long to transmit the tiny pink flickering image of a Maltese cross over a distance of two or three yards. This was the first image he had ever seen transmitted by television, and though but a tiny step forward, it was a tremendous encouragement to the struggling young inventor.

In *Master Minds of Modern Science* (published by Harrap) I note that the joint-authors, who give a first placc in thc volume to a brief survey of Baird's work, refer to this incident in these terms: "The authors believe that that first successful experiment at Hastings will be associated in History with the first electric light and the first flight of the Wright brothers."

Realising to the full the necessity of getting financial assistance, for at this stage his meagre funds were completely exhausted, Baird demonstrated these crude results to the Press. An account of his experiments appeared in the *Kinematograph Weekly* and attracted the attention of a certain Mr. Will Day, a London cinematograph proprietor, who wrote to Baird. In the meantime Baird had advertised in *The Times*, and among the replies which came to this advertisement was one from Mr. Odhams, Chairman of Odhams Press. Among those who had witnessed the demonstrations was the late Mr. William Le Queux, the famous novelist, who was a keen radio experimenter and who wrote accounts of Baird's work for the *Radio Times*.

At this time Baird developed the idea of forming a television company with himself, Mr. William Le Queux, Mr. Will Day, and Mr. Odhams. However, the idea did not come to fruition.

Mr. Day was very greatly fascinated by the project and the crude results that he witnessed, and eventually purchased from Baird a one-third interest in his invention for £200 cash. This provided funds for the experiments to continue and gave an impetus to the work.

EARLY EXPERIMENTS AT HASTINGS.

BAIRD WITH SOME OF THE EARLY APPARATUS USED IN HIS ATTIC AT 8, QUEENS ARCADE, HASTINGS, IN 1923, AS HE LABOURED ALONE & UNAIDED IN HIS STRUGGLES TO ACHIEVE TELEVISION.

COARSE SHADOWS TRANSMITTED.

BAIRD (CENTRE) DEMONSTRATING TO THE LATE MR. WILLIAM LE QUEUX (LEFT) THE APPARATUS BY MEANS OF WHICH HE TRANSMITTED COARSE SHADOWS AT HASTINGS IN 1924.

KINEMATOGRAPH WEEKLY APRIL 3, 1924

THE RADIO KINEMA

by F. H. ROBINSON

Not so very long ago I visited one John Logie Baird at his laboratory at Hastings. and saw a demonstration which proved that he has proceeded so far along the road to radio vision as to make it almost a commercial proposition, for the whole of the apparatus used in the experiment about to be described could have been purchased for £40.

The apparatus used can be applied to wire or wireless transmitters with ease and without the alteration of anything further than the microphone, in which circuit the "Radio Vision" machine is connected.

The Test.

I myself saw a cross, the letter "H," and the fingers of my own hand reproduced by this apparatus across the width of the laboratory. The images were quite sharp and clear, although perhaps a little unsteady. This, however, was mostly due to mechanical defects in the apparatus and not to any fault of the system.

Moving images may be transmitted by this means, and distance is no object, merely depending on the power of the wireless transmitter and the sensitivity of the receiver employed.

It is possible that machine-made apparatus on the lines indicated above could be made for some £50, which would be capable of transmitting letters and words clearly many miles through the ether, and all that appears to be necessary in order to reproduce and transmit moving pictures is more expensive and elaborate apparatus.

The inventor is confident that no technical difficulties stand in the way of the transmission of moving images by wireless.

Undoubtedly wonderful possibilities are opened up by this invention, its very simplicity and reliability placing it well to the front of many of the various complicated methods which have been evolved to do the same work.

A reproduction of one of the earliest press reports on Baird's work in Hastings. A brief extract from the article which induced Mr. Will Day to offer the first financial assistance which Baird received.

At this stage of the transmission of coarse shadows Baird was not alone in his achievement, for Jenkins, the well-known American experimenter, had done as much, while Mihaly claimed a similar feat. Up to this point it may be said that four nations were "in the running" in the International race for television—Britain, America, Austria, and France.

After further work Baird managed to get slightly improved results, and was able to transmit outline images of his apparatus, but it was uphill work all the time and once again funds were exhausted without any great advance being made. At this stage Baird sold a further one-sixth interest to Mr. Day, so that the invention now belonged one-half to Day and one-half to Baird.

It was now decided to bring the scene of activity to London, so in August 1924 Baird packed up all his makeshift gear and left the bracing air of Hastings which had restored him once again to health and vigour.

C H A P T E R   F I V E

STARVING IN LONDON

CHAPTER FIVE

STARVING IN LONDON

THE premises taken by Baird in London consisted of two attic rooms on the top floor of No. 22 Frith Street, that romantic street which leads from Shaftesbury Avenue to Soho Square, and has such a cosmopolitan population.

In these small rooms the crude apparatus was assembled and the experiments continued day by day. Progress was made, but it was heartbreakingly slow. However, gradually Baird advanced from the transmission of coarse shadowgraphs and succeeded in sending outlines of simple objects in black-and-white from one room to the other. What he could then achieve might in one sense be described as television, for it was the transmission of actual objects, although only in outline and in crude black-and-white effects, but television in the true sense of the word was really a long way off. In true television a real image must be sent with all gradations of light and shade.

In March 1925 Mr. Gordon Selfridge, junior, got to hear of these experiments, and after much inquiry traced the work to its source and called at the tiny attic laboratory. He was given a demonstration and saw transmitted from one room to the other a crude outline of a paper mask; this was made to wink by covering one of the eyeholes with white paper, and it could be made to open and close its mouth by covering and uncovering the slot corresponding to the mouth opening.

Mr. Selfridge, with the vision and enterprise associated with the great store which dominates Oxford Street, immediately visualised the immense potentialities of the invention from even the crude results seen and arranged for Baird to give personal demonstrations of the new device for three weeks at the Store. He agreed to pay the inventor £25 a week and supply the necessary electrical current and material.

This was a quite unexpected windfall which was accepted without delay, and in April 1925 Baird gave the first public exhibition of the transmission of outlines by wireless in Selfridge's Store. These shows were packed daily by scientists and general visitors from all parts of the country.

Those who looked for effect and were expecting to see fine examples of the cabinet-maker's and scientific instrument-maker's art were, of course, sadly disappointed. They saw a lens disc consisting

THE FIRST PUBLIC DEMONSTRATION OF TELEVISION

SELFRIDGE'S

Present the First Public

Demonstration of Television

in the Electrical Section (First Floor).

Television is to light what telephony is to sound—it means the *INSTANTANEOUS* transmission of a picture, so that the observer at the "receiving" end can see, to all intents and purposes, what is a cinematographic view of what is happening at the "sending" end.

For many years experiments have been conducted with this end in view; the apparatus that is here being demonstrated, is the first to be successful, and is as different to the apparatus that transmits pictures (that are from time to time printed in the newspapers) as the telephone is to the telegraph.

The apparatus here demonstrated is, of course, absolutely "in the rough"—the question of finance is always an important one for the inventor. But it does, undoubtedly, transmit an instantaneous picture. The picture is flickering and defective, and at present only simple pictures can be sent successfully ; but Edison's first phonograph announced that "Mary had a little lamb" in a way that only hearers who were "in the secret" could understand—and yet, from that first result has developed the gramophone of to-day. Unquestionably the present experimental apparatus can be similarly perfected and refined.

It has never before been shown to the Public. Mr. J. L. Baird, the sole inventor and owner of the patent rights, will be present daily while the apparatus is working—in the Electrical Section at 11.30 a.m., 2.30 p.m., and 3.15 p.m. He will be glad to explain to those interested in details.

We should perhaps explain that we are in no way financially interested in this remarkable invention ; the demonstrations are taking place here only because we know that our friends will be interested in something that should rank with the greatest iuventions of the century.

SELFRIDGE & CO., LTD.

A reproduction of a circular issued by Selfridge's in connection with Baird's public demonstration of the transmission of outlines by wireless, in April 1925.

of a circle cut from a cardboard box, the lenses being fixed between two layers of cardboard, while other parts of the apparatus showed the clear markings of a soap-box. The receiver consisted of a cardboard disc with sixteen holes arranged in two spirals. Synchronisation was obtained by using two little synchronous motors, one attached to the shaft of the transmitter and one to the shaft of the receiver, the motors being kept in step by a signal sent out from the transmitter which was used to control the receiver. Those interested will find that a full description of the apparatus was published in *Nature*, dated 4th April 1925.

Many people who gathered to watch this conglomeration of makeshift apparatus perform its marvellous task had but little notion of what it was all about, and the demonstrations gave rise to many inquiries and misgivings. It was thought that this weird machine heralded the disappearance of all privacy and was really a kind of marvellous telescope which could be focused on any desired spot and would show what was taking place round corners and behind brick walls.

After one demonstration a dear old lady took the inventor aside and inquired anxiously whether it would be possible to preserve privacy by pulling down the blinds while she was having a bath. There was, of course, absolutely no foundation for this alarm, for in a state of perfected television there must be a transmitting machine as well as a receiving machine and one could no more be seen without consent by television than one can be heard without consent by means of the telephone.

These demonstrations at Selfridge's showed only the transmission of outlines, and nothing in the shape of a human face, or any object containing light and shade and detail, could be transmitted. Television in the full sense of the word had not been accomplished. Many technical men who were present at this demonstration agreed that the results were very meritorious, but thought that years would elapse before it would be possible to transmit a living human face and recognise it.

It is interesting to note that it was just after these Selfridge demonstrations that Baird met his old school-friend, Jack Buchanan, who had now become a famous star of the theatrical world. Buchanan arranged a public dinner at Romano's at which his boyhood friend gave a demonstration of his television apparatus to members of the Press. Thus a friendship, broken for many years, was renewed, and since that date the two have frequently met, for Baird's headquarters have remained in the vicinity of Leicester Square, and consequently in the heart of the theatreland where the light of Jack Buchanan has shone so brightly.

Back went the apparatus to Frith Street, and by day and half the night Baird slaved to find the elusive missing link which he felt was almost within his grasp.

The cash from Selfridge's kept the enterprise running a little while longer, but soon that, too, was exhausted. Mr. Day by now was wondering when, if ever, he was going to get any financial return for the money he had invested in the project, and he did not feel justified in putting further money into the venture. The time came when there was a deadlock and it looked as though Baird would have to close down and abandon the whole business.

In the face of all discouragement the now penniless Baird made desperate efforts to carry on his lonely experiments. He had come to the bleakest, blackest, period of his career—the darkest hour before the dawn!

Baird was now existing in most abject poverty, at times he literally denied himself bread to carry on the work. In the face of semi-starvation his frail constitution again gave him trouble. He roamed the streets of London in threadbare clothing, with the socks showing through the soles of the old boots that he could not afford to have repaired.

He called at several newspaper offices and tried to arouse interest in his apparatus, but was taken as one of the many cranks who regard the Press as the dumping ground for the most insane ideas. He was either ejected as a charlatan or soothed off the premises as a madman.

It seemed that in all London nobody had any real interest in television. Nobody wanted to hear about it. Nobody was interested in this thin, pale young Scotsman who cut such a perfect picture of the traditional stage inventor starving in a garret—and the tragedy was that this inventor *was* quite literally starving in a garret. It was no stage play.

Among the efforts Baird made in this trying period was the flotation of a small company to get the venture out of difficulties. He advertised in the Press for a company promoter to assist in the formation of a small private limited company to finance an invention for seeing by wireless.

The result of this advertisement was that the tiny laboratory was deluged by a small army of would-be company promoters. As Baird said, he had seldom seen such an array of dilapidated white

AN HISTORIC PHOTOGRAPH.

AN UNTOUCHED PHOTOGRAPH OF A HUMAN FACE AS IT APPEARED ON THE RECEIVING SCREEN OF THE FIRST BAIRD "TELEVISOR" IN 1926, THE YEAR WHEN TRUE TELEVISION WAS FIRST ACHIEVED.

TRANSMISSION OF OUTLINES.

EARLY IN 1925 BAIRD WAS ABLE TO DEMONSTRATE THE TRANSMISSION OF OUTLINES IN BLACK & WHITE WITH THIS APPARATUS IN HIS ATTIC ROOMS AT 22, FRITH STREET, LONDON.

spats and frayed striped trousers! These company promoters, with one exception, had a *sine qua non*, and that was that Baird must advance them a certain amount of cash for preliminary expenses. Baird had no cash and therefore there was no business.

The one exception was a Mr. Brooks, who realised that Baird could not part with what he had not got. Baird's idea at this time was to circularise all the medical profession, and he had drafted a letter which began: "Dear Sir or Madam,—For the past three years I have been experimenting in an endeavour to transmit living images by wireless. These experiments have resulted in a certain measure of success," and so on. Baird and Brooks stamped, addressed and despatched three thousand letters to the medical profession, each letter enclosing a post card asking the recipient to state if he was interested and would like a representative to call.

From these three thousand letters seven replies only were received, and Mr. Brooks called on the seven, the agreement being no results no expenses. This scheme had little useful result and was finally abandoned.

Things were now so critical that at last Baird could not pay the small rental of his two attic

ORIGINAL TELEVISION APPARATUS

Made by J. L. BAIRD, Esq.

This is the transmitting portion of the original apparatus used by Mr. J. L. Baird in experiments which led him from the wireless transmission of outlines in 1925 to the achievement of true television nine months later, when, on 27th January 1926, the transmission of living human faces with light, shade and detail was demonstrated before members of the Royal Institution, this being the first demonstration of true television ever given.

One can only wonder what can be the inner feelings of John Logie Baird about the darkest chapter in his career, when he stands beside this historic case in the museum wherein is preserved for the nation that first crude apparatus, to improve which he risked his health, wore the soles from his shoes and denied himself bread!

CHAPTER SIX

TRUE TELEVISION AT LAST

CHAPTER SIX

TRUE TELEVISION AT LAST!

IT was on 2nd October 1925 that Baird had what was then, and still is, the greatest thrill of his lifetime.

The previous evening he had concluded a series of most exhaustive tests with the latest of the numerous light-sensitive systems he had devised, and, *in theory*, it seemed that this one should prove the key to the problem when fitted for a practical test. However, he had so frequently met disappointment in the past, owing to theories failing to materialise in practice, that no unbounded hopes were raised on this occasion.

The morning was spent in fitting the device and generally overhauling the apparatus, and early on this Friday afternoon he placed "Bill" in front of the transmitter. "Bill," it should be explained, was a rather dilapidated ventriloquist's doll that Baird had used for many months in his experiments, its use being necessitated by the absence of any human assistance whatever. When carrying out tests from one room to another Baird obviously could not be at both ends at once, and it was this doll which was seated regularly at the transmitting end wearing a perpetual fatuous grin.

Normally this doll's head came through on the receiving screen as a white blob with three black blobs marking the position of nose and eyes, but on this never-to-be-forgotten afternoon, after a preliminary run of the apparatus, the features of "Bill" suddenly appeared on the receiving screen before Baird. Not a black-and-white effect, but a real recognisable image with shading and detail—the nose, eyes, and eyebrows could be distinguished and the top of the head appeared rounded.

Television was achieved at last!

This young Scotsman, after nearly two years' struggle under the most disheartening conditions throughout, had, single-handed, wrested yet another secret from Nature's storehouse.

Flushed with success, Baird's normal phlegmatic calm momentarily deserted him in this supreme triumph. His first thought was to get a living model to place before the transmitter and dashing out of the room he tore madly downstairs. His own explanation of this action was that he was "vastly excited."

William Taynton, a young office boy, working for a Mr. Cross on the floor below, was rather surprised to have burst in upon him the "inventor fellow" from the floor above, with a shirt open at the neck, ancient flannel "bags," carpet slippers and no socks, and an amazingly tangled shock of hair over his eyes now starting out with excitement. In a flood of excited broad Scotch this apparition tried to convey some urgent reason why the lad should come upstairs immediately.

Taynton was naturally rather reluctant to commit himself to any experiment conducted by this excitable Scot, but at last Baird persuaded him to come upstairs and sit before the transmitter where enormous electric lamps gave out a glaring light, and a great deal of heat.

Baird rushed to the next room to see what results would appear on the screen. It was entirely blank and no amount of tuning would produce any results. After some minutes Baird went back to the transmitter very puzzled and disappointed, and there the cause of failure became evident. The office boy had moved back a little to avoid the intensely bright light and heat and had, of course, moved out of focus.

In what Baird always describes as "the excitement of the moment" he gave the boy half a crown and explained that he must remain exactly as placed. Presumably overcome at receiving a tip from a Scotsman, Taynton obeyed him to the letter this time! His image appeared on the receiving screen.

Just as the lad was feeling that he could not keep still a moment longer, Baird shouted from the next room and told him to open his mouth, and then to turn the head to one side.

Baird now came back and suggested that they should change places. This was done, and as Baird sat before the transmitter, Taynton, looking through the little square opening at the receiving end, saw Baird's face swaying in a reddish light. It was not very clear, but he was able to see the mouth open and close, and finally to recognise the image as that of Mr. Baird.

Thus, William Taynton, who I noticed recently is now employed by the Baird Television Company, goes down to history as the first person in the world to be seen by television, although it is rather curious to consider that it should have required a bribe to induce him to accept this distinction. He was also the second person in the world to see a televised human face.

Baird now put in further enthusiastic work in his laboratory in order definitely to consolidate the position he had won and to ensure that the amazing result achieved was stable and not but a freak of

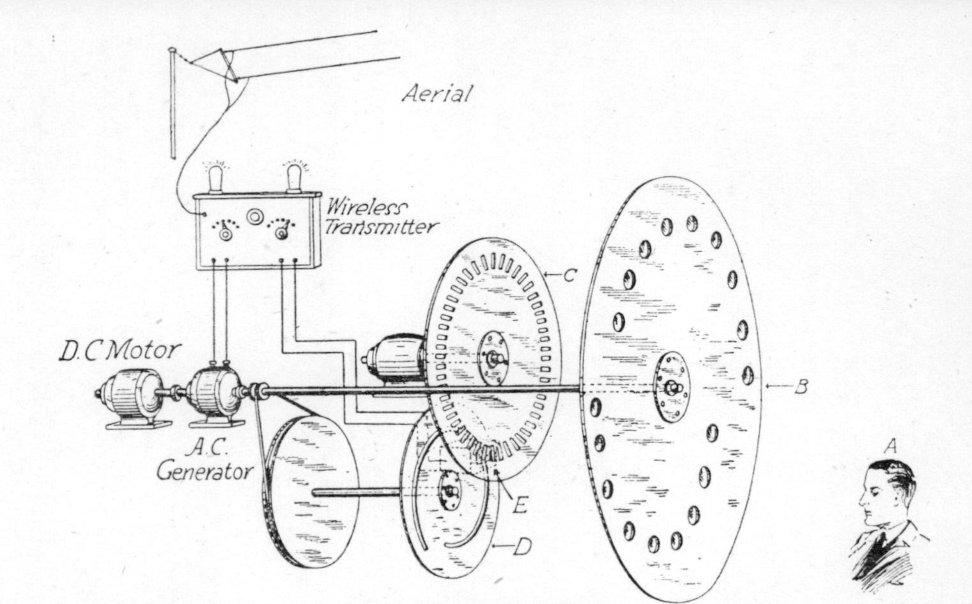

Baird's Original Transmitter

A. Person to be transmitted. B. Revolving disc with lenses. C. Slotted disc revolving at high speed. D. Rotating spiral slot. E. Aperture through which light passes to light-sensitive cell.

chance. Finally, he had the apparatus ready to demonstrate in public and chose in the first place to demonstrate to a critical, scientific audience.

He issued the now historic invitation to the members of the Royal Institution of Great Britain, one of our leading scientific societies, and having worded the invitation rather recklessly in view of his restricted accommodation, found an unusual crowd thronging the stairway and corridors of the Frith Street building on 27th January 1926. Nearly fifty scientists, young and old, attended this demonstration.

Owing to the confined space available, members entered the laboratory in batches of half a dozen, while on the stairs outside Mr. W. C. Fox, a journalist who was attracted by Baird's work in early days, endeavoured to entertain the overflow. The transmission of living human faces from one room to the other was achieved beyond a shadow of doubt.

This was the first public demonstration of true television to be given in the history of the world—an important and authenticated fact which may readily be verified from numerous accessible records. Before 27th January 1926 nothing but the transmission of simple outlines and silhouettes had ever been demonstrated in any country.

In view of unsupported reports of television "systems" which have appeared from time to time in the past, it is as well to make it quite clear that there is a world of difference between a "claim" and an actual public demonstration.

There was sufficient proof forthcoming of Baird's epoch-making achievement to satisfy even the most sceptical. In *The Times* of 28th January 1926 the following account of the demonstration appeared:

"Members of the Royal Institution and other visitors to a laboratory in an upper room in Frith Street, Soho, on Tuesday saw a demonstration of apparatus invented by Mr. J. L. Baird. . . .

"For the purpose of the demonstration the head of a ventriloquist's doll was manipulated as the image to be transmitted, though the human face was also reproduced. First on a receiver in the same room as the transmitter, and then on a portable receiver in another room, the visitors were shown recognisable reception of the movements of the dummy head and of a person speaking. The image as transmitted was faint and often blurred, but substantiated a claim that through the 'Televisor,' as Mr. Baird has named his apparatus, it is possible to transmit and reproduce instantly the details of movement, and such things as the play of expression on the face."

In the United States, where great interest in television is manifest, Baird's achievement was fully acknowledged. *Radio News*, one of their foremost

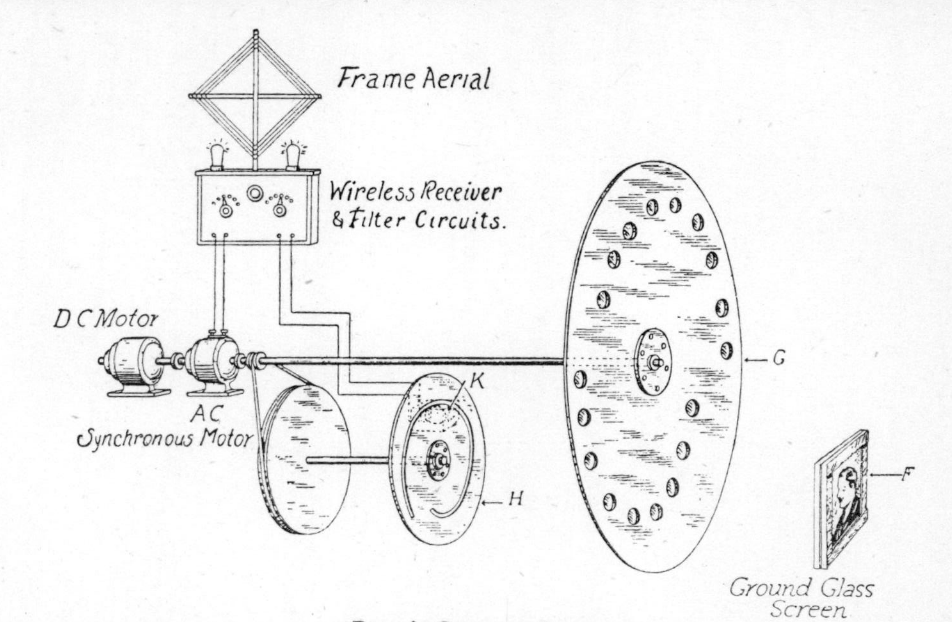

BAIRD'S ORIGINAL RECEIVER

F. Reproduced image. G. Revolving disc with lenses. H. Rotating spiral slot. K. The aperture through which the light passes from the varying light source.

journals, sent a commissioner to investigate his results, and in their issue of September 1926 stated: "Mr. Baird has definitely and indisputably given a demonstration of real television. It is the first time in history that this has been done in any part of the world." Furthermore, in an article on television in the *New York Times* of 6th March 1927, reference was made to the fact that "no one but this Scotch minister's son has ever transmitted and received a recognisable image with its gradations of light and shade." While in an editorial in the same paper for 11th February 1928 we see: "Baird was the first to achieve television."

I stress this evidence respecting the end of the International race for the honour of achieving television, because after enduring so much in the vicissitudes recorded in this narrative it is only right that to John Logie Baird should be accorded this distinction without shadow of doubt.

It was early in 1926 that Baird had the good fortune, while walking in the Strand, to meet an old business associate, Captain Oliver George Hutchinson, who at one time had been his rival in the soap business. Baird's "Speedy Cleanser" had been in competition with Hutchinson's "Rapid Washer," and in fact Hutchinson and Baird had been about to form a soap combine when Baird had been compelled to leave the field by his breakdown in health.

Captain Hutchinson went to Frith Street and was enthusiastic at what he witnessed. Together with a friend, Captain Broadrip, he bought out Mr. Will Day's interest, as that gentleman had now grown tired of waiting for a return on his capital and needed it for the development of his own business.

Geniuses are notoriously uncommercial, but Baird, a level-headed Scot with commercial experience, was somewhat of an exception in this respect. At the same time it was good fortune that brought Hutchinson and Baird together at this stage, for Hutchinson took over the business side of the venture with all the extraordinary energy of his vigorous Irish personality. It is largely due to his efforts that British television occupies the position it does to-day, both here and in other countries.

Captain Hutchinson introduced fresh capital into the venture immediately, and Baird's relatives in Scotland provided further funds, so in February 1926 a move was made to Motograph House, near Leicester Square.

At this new address Baird had more space at his disposal, his financial difficulties were eased, thus permitting more elaborate laboratory equipment, and with the conduct of the business side of the enterprise safely entrusted to Captain Hutchinson, the inventor was enabled to devote his whole time and energy to improving his apparatus. Wireless masts appeared on the roof of the building and research work proceeded apace upon certain definite and well-conceived lines.

It was not until now that Baird knew the "luxury" of employing a staff. Hitherto all his work had been conducted absolutely alone. At Motograph House he engaged his first staff—an office boy who was also general assistant! Towards the end of 1926 he employed his first technical assistant, a Mr. Clapp, who is still serving under him. From that date his technical staff has grown to twenty-two in number.

The steady research work now led to gradually improved results and many demonstrations were given by Baird during 1926 at Motograph House to Press representatives and others. The images of living faces were transmitted, and received with every gradation of light and shade, from the transmitter on the top floor to a small receiving "theatre" several floors below. Thus in *Nature*, dated 3rd July 1926, Dr. Russell, F.R.S., the principal of Faraday House, wrote:

"We saw the transmission by television of living human faces, the proper gradation of light and shade, and all movements of the head, of the lips and mouth, and of a cigarette and its smoke were faithfully portrayed on a screen in the theatre, the transmitter being in a room at the top of the building. Naturally, the results are far from perfect. The image cannot be compared with that produced by a good Kinematograph film. The likeness, however, was unmistakable, and all the motions are reproduced with absolute fidelity. This is the first time we have seen real television, and, so far as we know, Mr. Baird is the first to have accomplished this marvellous feat."

Other evidence of the progress that resulted from Baird's unceasing work at this time is found in the *Daily Telegraph*:

"A member of the Press was persuaded to submit himself to the transmitting end of the apparatus in the laboratory under three lamps of 2000 candle-power each, and at the receiving end he was recognised by his colleagues. . . . The image of his face was sharply defined; when he opened his mouth the movement was clearly seen, and when he spoke into the telephone his lips could be seen pronouncing every word, while the sound was conveyed to the audience by means of a loud speaker. The image, we may add, was far brighter, clearer, and larger than it was at the demonstration three months ago."

While at the beginning of 1926 Baird could show a recognisable image of a human face, his improvements later in the year permitted larger images of the complete head and shoulders to be sent.

Another advance he made was in the reduction of the lighting necessary at the transmitter, for at first the batteries of electric lamps used were so powerful as to almost burn and blind the person sitting before them. Even stage folk, accustomed to the glare of limelight, found it an extremely uncomfortable procedure to be televised, but gradually this glare was reduced to normal room lighting standard.

Although I had corresponded with the late Mr. William Le Queux on the subject of Baird's Hastings experiments, and had also communicated with Baird early in 1926, it was not until the early summer of that year that I first met the inventor face to face at Motograph House. I had been sent by the editor of a weekly journal to record my impressions of the man, his apparatus, and his results, and on keeping an appointment I was met by an office-boy who informed me that Mr. Baird was "In there," indicating a closed door.

Entering the room I found myself in a very primitive laboratory, a rough work-bench of unpolished white-wood ran round the walls and was crowded with most mysterious equipment. The hum of high-power electrical apparatus was plainly discernible, and I had difficulty in finding a spot on the dusty floor clear of the amazing tangle of wires that crossed and re-crossed.

The office-boy's pronouncement regarding the whereabouts of the man I sought appeared to be founded upon misapprehension, for the room was empty.

Then, right at my feet, a scuffle and dislocation of dust startled me. Turning round I beheld two grubby check carpet slippers emerging from under a bench. Then came bare ankles, dusty flannel trousers, a grey flannel shirt devoid of collar, and the mysterious individual stood up.

No introduction was necessary; I had interrupted Mr. Baird at his work.

In appearance Baird had the pale complexion of a scholar, behind his spectacles the eyes of a dreamer, and a spare but agile frame full of nervous energy. His head was crowned with a most amazing shock of tangled light brown hair, while his very slow and cautious speech clearly betrayed his country of origin. His sheer simplicity of manner and courtesy of welcome attracted instantly, and with the modestly recounted details he gave in response to my questioning, quickly revealed the keynote of his character.

Since that date I have been a privileged visitor

in Mr. Baird's laboratory and have gained first-hand knowledge of the many developments which have taken place there. I have also observed him in his dealings with all classes of people, under all sorts of conditions, and see no reason to this date to modify my original impression of his character.

CHAPTER SEVEN

PRODUCTS OF A FERTILE BRAIN

CHAPTER SEVEN

PRODUCTS OF A FERTILE BRAIN

AS previously mentioned, in the earliest television demonstrations Baird was obliged to use intensely brilliant lighting, and one of the first things he concentrated on, in an effort to bring his apparatus to commercial success, was the reduction of this. Soon he had succeeded in achieving similar results with but the use of normal lighting, and this was a decided advance.

At this time it occurred to him that he was dealing not with the human eye in his apparatus, but with a sensitive electric one which might detect rays outside the comparatively limited range of human eyesight. First he experimented with ultra-violet rays, but they proved unsatisfactory owing to the unpleasant effect upon the skin and eyes of those being transmitted. They also had little penetration power, being quickly absorbed after passing through air.

Baird next turned his attention to the other end of the spectrum, which is called the infra-red and is outside the range of the human eye. The ordinary photo-electric cell is almost unaffected by these rays, but he evolved a new light-sensitive device which was sensitive to infra-red rays and without inertia. This system worked perfectly, and he was able to dispense altogether with visible light and to produce one of the most amazing developments of modern time—seeing a person at a distance in total darkness!

The first public announcement of this sensational advance was made in the London *Daily Mail* in December 1926, following a special demonstration arranged for two of their representatives. The following is an extract from their published experience:

"In the demonstration my colleague sat in darkness before the transmitting screen of the 'televisor.' Above his head, shut off by an enclosed space from the room, were a certain number of ordinary electric lights. The rays from these impinged upon a light filter.

"This filter extracted everything that was visible from these rays, and only allowed to pass into the room certain rays in the lower spectrum invisible to the human eye. These unseen rays bathed my colleague's head and shoulders, without his being in the least conscious of the fact, and after they had been 'analysed' by the apparatus in front of the transmitter, were flashed by wireless across an intervening empty room to the sensitive cell in Mr. Baird's 'televisor.' This was installed in a third room; it had been adapted specially to receive these rays and to project them in a visible form upon a screen.

"In the receiving room I sat in total darkness before the small screen. On it flickered and then clarified an easily recognisable head-and-shoulders of my colleague as he sat in the other room in the pitch-black dark. He turned his head, as we had agreed he should, opened and shut his eyes, and drew back and then approached nearer. The fidelity of the image was perfect. I was accomplishing the apparent miracle of seeing a distant person in the dark who was illuminated by a ray invisible to the human eye."

Baird again issued an invitation to members of the Royal Institution, and about forty of them came to the laboratory to witness tests of this new discovery which the inventor christened "Noctovision," and the apparatus with which it was achieved the "Noctovisor." It was discovered quite by accident that these infra-red rays had valuable fog-penetration powers. In a demonstration of television a certain Press representative noticed the smoke curling upwards from a cigarette as viewed on the screen; when he called to see Noctovision demonstrated he asked for a cigarette to be smoked and it was found that the rising smoke was invisible.

By the development of this "black light," following so closely on the television demonstrations, Baird clearly established his position as an inventive genius of the first water, and the many other wonders which have since sprung from that fertile brain have but served to consolidate that position in the eyes of the world.

Baird's success in the television field naturally caused his contemporaries to redouble their efforts, and in April 1927 the American Telephone and Telegraph Company staged the first television demonstration to be given out of England. Images were sent by wire for a distance of 200 miles between New York and Washington, the whole experiment being staged with great elaboration and occupying the services of 1000 engineers.

The British inventor made no comment on the American test which achieved so much publicity. He just went quietly to work and towards the end of May 1927 he arranged a demonstration of television over the 438 miles of telephone line between London and Glasgow—easily a world's record transmission. It was repeated on two following nights.

The transmission was carried out from Baird's London Office, and the receiver was installed in a room at the Central Hotel, Glasgow. An important point in connection with this demonstration was that Baird used two operators only, one at either end. Two telephone lines were utilised, one for vision and one for speech, and the scientists and business men watching in Glasgow were much impressed with the results seen on the receiving screen. Baird put his office boy before the transmitter in London and later was persuaded to appear himself, and his features were immediately recognised by friends in the North.

Professor Taylor Jones, of Glasgow University, commented in *Nature* (18th June 1927) on the test he had seen:

"The image was perfectly steady in position, was remarkably free from distortion, and showed no sign of the 'streakiness' which was, I believe, in evidence in the earlier experiments. . . . The image was sufficiently bright to be seen vividly even when the electric light in the room was switched on, and I understand that there was no difficulty in enlarging the image to full size. . . . The amount of light and shade shown in the image was amply sufficient to secure recognisability of the person being 'televised,' and movements of the face or features were clearly seen. . . . My impression after witnessing the demonstrations is that the chief difficulties connected with television have been overcome by Mr. Baird, and that the improvements still to be effected are mainly matters of detail. . . ."

During 1927 Baird was working steadily to improve the results of his television system, and the received images I saw from time to time showed marked, though gradual, improvements. He was also improving his "Noctovision" apparatus, and at the British Association meeting at Leeds in September he gave demonstrations of this from one room to another and many hundreds witnessed the demonstrations.

During the course of these tests Baird stated, quite modestly and simply, that although he was showing merely from one room to another the distance between transmitter and receiver was, of course, of no object, subject to reasonable limitations. In an article written at the time a critic raised doubts on this point, but when Baird made such a statement he was speaking with his natural native caution. On this occasion, as on many subsequent ones, he declined to enter into any controversy, but produced the proofs of his statement.

Without any delay he staged long-distance "Noctovision" demonstrations over the 170 miles of telephone wire between Leeds and London. On the evening of 7th September 1927 I was invited to witness one of the tests. Entering a darkened room in the building near Leicester Square I sat before

BAIRD WITH THE AUTHOR, 1927.

PHOTOGRAPHED IN THE FORMER'S LABORATORY IN 1927 WITH AN EARLY "TELEVISOR" DESIGNED TO RECEIVE BOTH SIGHTS AND SOUNDS.

BAIRD WITH SIR OLIVER LODGE.

THE FIRST MAN IN THE WORLD TO DEMONSTRATE TRUE TELEVISION PHOTOGRAPHED WHILE CHATTING WITH SIR OLIVER LODGE AT THE BRITISH ASSOCIATION MEETING AT LEEDS IN 1927.

a cabinet inset in which was a panel of frosted glass, roughly a foot square. The apparatus hummed into life and then a streak of whirling orange light appeared in the glass panel. In this band of light, as synchronising adjustments were made, the flickering image of a human face appeared about two inches square fairly clearly—that of a man seated in total darkness in Leeds. Over the other telephone line I conversed with Mr. Baird and asked for various movements of the head and features to be made, and the screen immediately showed obedience. An uncanny demonstration conjured up by the fertile brain of a modern wizard.

It was following these Leeds demonstrations that the Television Society of Great Britain was formed, with the late Lord Haldane as its first President, and many distinguished men on the Council. This Society made Baird an Honorary Fellow in recognition of his outstanding television achievements.

During 1927 Baird was operating 2.T.V., the world's first television transmitting station, and at all hours of the night he would be personally conducting tests in the wireless transmission of images from Motograph House, London, to a receiving station at "Green Gables," Harrow, a distance of about twelve miles. Wireless amateurs who tuned in these transmissions on 200 metres at this time were very mystified to pick up on their receivers a high-pitched "me-me-me-me" as they received the *sounds* of an image being transmitted.

Towards the end of 1927 the centre of Baird's activities had been moved to Long Acre, London. It is from the Studios at this address the television programmes broadcast by the B.B.C. in the past year or so have been given.

At the end of the year the subject of television was arousing sufficient interest for a group of business men to decide to publish the world's first television journal, and I was invited to organise and control this publication. Other activities prevented me accepting, but as the first acting editor I spent two interesting months preparing the initial number. In order to prevent possible competition the scheme was kept secret from all but the necessary few, and as a result I wrote and prepared practically all the issue single-handed in an office taken in my name. On publication in March 1928 the permanent staff took over and the journal has flourished to this day.

I mention this episode because it was in connection with it that I no doubt tried Mr. Baird sorely at this stage. He was a very busy man, but I interrupted his work time and time again, bullying and badgering him for demonstrations, explanations, assistance, and advice. His stock of patience proved inexhaustible, and I had striking proof of the innate kindliness of his nature.

CHAPTER EIGHT

A RECORD OF ACHIEVEMENT

REALISING the necessity of demonstrating conclusively the value of television in bridging space, Baird patiently and unostentatiously worked on radio transmissions from a private experimental station at Coulsdon, Surrey, and a few of us knew that his ambition was to be "first across" the Atlantic, as he worked long through the night hours.

On the 9th February 1928 he startled the world by achieving his objective, and persons seated in London were seen clearly in New York. At midnight, London time, the image of a ventriloquist's doll was set before the transmitter at Long Acre, sent by land line to Coulsdon and thence transmitted across the Atlantic on a wave-length of 45 metres. The signals were picked up by an amateur operating a station at Hartsdale, a few miles from New York, and the experimental receiver installed showed the image on the ground-glass screen about three inches square, in the presence of Reuter's Press representative and others.

When the doll had been tuned clearly a message

rapidly moving dots and lines of orange light which gradually formed themselves into a definitely recognisable face. This image varied from time to time in clarity, but movements could be clearly seen, and the image, when clear, was unmistakable."

This transmission to the *Berengaria* took place with the normal wireless work of the ship going on, and the receiver remained unaffected by the vibrations and rolling of the vessel, and the test certainly suggested that in time to come passengers on long sea voyages should have little difficulty in keeping in visual as well as vocal touch with those left behind.

Baird's progress continued unabated, thanks to his untiring energy and a continued capacity for hard work. He still put in very long hours in the laboratory at this time, and I have left there as late as 9 o'clock at night and left him still working on a problem started early in the morning. It was quite exceptional for him to take even a week-end rest from the beloved research work. It is small wonder that after paying a lengthy call on Baird in June 1928 no less an authority than Sir Ambrose Fleming, F.R.S., the famous inventor of the thermionic valve, wrote of his visit: ". . . the writer left the laboratory with the strong conviction that it was the birthplace of new, interesting, and very important inventions."

Early in June 1928 Baird achieved a most important advance and was the first man to give public demonstrations of television in daylight, thus rendering it unnecessary to have any rapidly moving beams of light or brilliant illumination of any sort. Any normal daylight sufficient for a photograph to be taken was enough for him to show clear images of people posed before the special transmitter fitted on the flat roof of the Long Acre building, and this step obviously brought the day nearer when it would be possible to televise a horse race and outdoor scenes. I saw Baird's old school-friend, Jack Buchanan, call in and pose on the roof in immaculate white flannels during the course of the demonstrations.

Writing in *Television* for August 1928, Major A. Church, B.Sc., the General Secretary of the Association of Scientific Workers, stated:

"On 18th June I was again invited to the Long Acre laboratory to further demonstrations. In the first one the persons were seated on the roof in front of the transmitter, the object being illuminated only by daylight. (Incidentally it was an exceptionally dull day.) At the receiver I had no difficulty in distinguishing between the features of one person and another, or in detecting their slightest movements; there was, in fact, more detail observable than I had seen in the February demonstration when the object was artificially illuminated."

Hard on the heels of these daylight demonstrations Baird secured yet another record, and in July 1928 was the first man to demonstrate television in natural colours. I saw striking demonstrations in which the vivid reality of the colourings seen on the receiving screen was quite remarkable. When the human face was transmitted it showed a delicate pink, while a protruding tongue showed in deeper pink, the subject also tied scarves of various colours round the head and then placed on a policeman's blue helmet, and each colour came through clearly. A bunch of blue flowers, and another of red roses, appeared in amazingly vivid fashion and as near the original shades as could be determined.

In the following month Baird was able to demonstrate stereoscopic television for the first time and thus show images not as though a flat picture on a screen, but as a solid object with length, breadth, and depth. In this respect Dr. C. Tierney, D.Sc., wrote in *Television* for September 1928:

"On 9th August, in company with Prof. Cheshire and others, I visited the Baird laboratories and witnessed the first demonstration of stereoscopic television. A man sitting before the transmitter was very clearly seen on the screen of a receiver situated in another part of the building, in perfect relief, showing the facial delineation and expression both with and without optical assistance. These experiments promise considerable development and importance in their practical application."

This brief and simple historical survey of the stream of developments which sprang from the fertile brain of the British television pioneer within a short period all serves to illustrate Baird's genius in the selection of essentials in experimentation. Throughout the same period the ordinary television research went on and conditions at both transmitting and receiving end were considerably improved. It was now no ordeal whatever to face the transmitter, in fact whereas my first broadcast from a B.B.C. studio at Savoy Hill was marked by most unpleasant "mike-fright" (the broadcasters' equivalent of stage fright), I was quite at home in the Baird studio on the occasions when I was "televised" during tests.

Baird had been living for some time at a boarding-house in Finchley Road, London, but with poverty and privation an unpleasant episode of the past, in May 1929 he took a lease of one of the most beautiful little cottages in the south of England, "The Swiss Cottage" perched right on the crest of Boxhill, Surrey. This was at one time the shooting-box of the Duke of Marlborough, and the house contains many interesting relics. It is said that one of the first Dukes, who was a delicate infant, was brought up here in complete seclusion, and the house and grounds are completely surrounded by remarkable box hedges several hundreds of years old. Visitors to the neighbourhood would know the house, as just outside the gates is the extraordinary grave of Peter Labiere, an eccentric resident of Dorking who, according to the old tombstone, was buried standing upright. The windows of the house look down the glorious Dorking valley and provide a wonderful view by day and a most striking spectacle at night.

Here Baird had a private electrical plant and all the necessities for carrying out many of his private experiments in complete seclusion and peace, and he stayed there until removal to North London in March 1932.

By the autumn of 1928 the first commercial television apparatus had been designed and Baird chose the occasion of the National Radio Exhibition at Olympia, London, W., to show these and his system to the general public. No demonstrations were permitted in Olympia itself, so premises were hired close by, and throughout the week hundreds of people struggled to view the demonstrations. Combined sight-and-sound receivers were utilised, the loud speaker being fitted one side of the cabinet and the ten-inch circular viewing screen on the other.

The results that Baird showed his visitors here were remarkable. On the receiving screen one saw the head and shoulders of the person being televised, the eyelashes could be seen, dimples distinguished, the teeth counted and every slight play of expression readily observed. I was reporting the tests for one of the London daily papers and spent the entire week with Baird, so my impressions were first hand.

On the afternoon of the first day Miss Peggy O'Neil, the popular actress, who was then starring at the Lyceum Theatre, visited the demonstration. She was received very shyly by Mr. Baird, not quite so shyly by myself, and not at all shyly by Captain Hutchinson. After watching reception for a time we persuaded her to go to the transmitter housed next door, then as her charming and familiar features appeared on the receiving screen Miss O'Neil gave us nearly half an hour of real entertainment, singing fascinating songs and telling droll Irish stories. I have never seen features televise better before or since, and her show gave a vivid impression of the potentialities of Baird's system as an entertainment force. On other days various stage celebrities, including Harry Tate and his son and Miss Lilian Davies, appeared and gave performances over the system.

However, from Baird's point of view it may be said that Miss Peggy O'Neil's performance was of great importance, for it was this turn that was witnessed by Mr. Sydney A. Moseley, a well-known and popular figure in Fleet Street. This was, I understand, Moseley's first lengthy examination of Baird's results, and he was so tremendously impressed by the potentialities of the art that he became one of its staunchest champions. Soon afterwards he joined the Board of Television Press and took over control of the *Television* magazine for a time.

While Baird was passing through the next twelve trying months, the story of which forms another chapter, it was Moseley who gave the spirited support of his virile and facile pen to Baird and who strove wholeheartedly to right what he genuinely believed to be an injustice.

During the public demonstrations one other record was established, for it occurred to me to secure a *Daily Mail* Contents Bill and ask Baird to televise it. He passed it slowly before the trans-

"DAILY MAIL" TELEVISED.

CONTENTS BILL SEEN THROUGH BRICK WALLS.

A *Daily Mail* contents bill was seen at a distance through several brick walls yesterday at the public demonstrations of the British television system which are being given during Radio Exhibition week at Olympia, Kensington, W.

Mr. R. F. Tiltman, a television expert, suggested that an attempt should be made to send moving lettering by television. He obtained a *Daily Mail* contents bill from a newsagent and had it sent to the transmitting studio a short distance down the road.

A few moments later the person being televised announced through the loud speakers, "We will now show you the contents bill of a London daily newspaper."

The image of the sitter faded from the reception screen, and gradually from the blur of orange light emerged in bold type the word "Daily." This moved across to the left and gave place to "Mail" The rustling of the bill could be heard from the loud speakers as the audience read from the slowly moving letters "24 Pages Again : County Prize Beauties Pictures."

The wording could be clearly read, and this hastily arranged test may be said to constitute the first advertisement to be sent by television in the world.

The three receivers were of the standard commercial type. A grill on the left concealed the loud speaker, and on the right was mounted a circular viewing screen about 12 inches across, on the lighted portion of which the *Daily Mail* lettering appeared.

A Cutting from the "Daily Mail"
Describing how the author aided Baird to transmit the world's first advertisement by television.

CHAPTER NINE

DISPARAGEMENT RUNS RIFE

CHAPTER NINE

DISPARAGEMENT RUNS RIFE

THE autumn of 1928 saw the opening of a year of strife over the vexed question of broadcasting facilities which would place Baird's achievements before the public in programme form—and Baird himself had to pass through a most trying time with the air full of lies, half-truths, and baseless criticism levelled by many so-called "experts" at the product of his genius.

I commence this chapter with no desire to probe unnecessarily old wounds in these days of peaceful advancement. A few individuals who carried their "King Canute" attitude to the last before final submersion by the irresistible advance of the television waves would, no doubt, prefer certain facts to remain as a closed book of the past. At the same time no life-story of John L. Baird could be complete which did not refer briefly to this difficult period through which he had to pass and its reaction upon his character.

Britain has so few records to its credit in these days that it would be not unreasonable to imagine that when the brilliant research work of a pioneer was able to secure for this country every world record in a branch of science of obviously vast potentialities, the whole nation would unite in an effort to see that the leadership was maintained. As Major Church wrote in August 1928: "The possibilities of television are so immense that it should have been regarded as a question of national honour to have backed substantially any inventor whose discovery in this field was based on the established laws of science and whose results could be demonstrated."

Yet while Baird's achievements were recognised to the full in foreign countries, and by foreign visitors to his laboratory, in his own land for some time he was met with most disheartening apathy and obstruction by sections of the Press and the people.

Distinguished visitors from abroad who called on Baird recorded their whole-hearted enthusiasm in his visitors' book after seeing his work at this time. In *Television* for December 1928 Dr. F. Gradenwitz wrote of a second visit to Baird:

"Unquestionably the Baird system is immensely in advance of any system on the Continent. I had, of course, expected to find television greatly improved since I was here last year; I expected better definition and more detail, but I was not prepared to see the progress that has actually been made. . . . Everything has definitely outgrown the experimental stage and was in a form which could safely be put in the hands of the wireless amateur or the man in the street. In Germany every encouragement is being given to research workers in television. . . . In view of this fact I am amazed at the attitude of the British Broadcasting Corporation. . . . It seems to be extraordinary that a British invention should be unable to obtain facilities for its development in the country of its birth."

Commander Brenot, Chief Engineer of Radio-Paris, indeed the leading French wireless engineer, visited Baird about this time and was shown sufficient to cause him to write: "The first industrial apparatus of television. What Mr. Baird has achieved is far ahead of what the most optimistic spirits could have dared thinking only a year ago at the International Wireless Conference held in Washington." Another guest of Baird's was Mr. E. Svoboda, Technical Manager of the Czechoslovakian Broadcasting Service, who stated: "I have no doubt in my mind from what I have just seen here in London that television has definitely reached a commercial stage."

At precisely the same time Baird had to face a barrage of attacks made upon his work by arm-

further development, but the achievements to date have a scientific basis, and television's record so far compares not unfavourably with the initial stages of the phonograph or gramophone, or with photography, wireless telegraphy, or telephony and electrical illumination at a similar age, and all of these were regarded at their first start as unpractical or useless curiosities. . . . That recognisable images of moving and living objects such as human faces have been transmitted even to large distances by wire and by wireless, by Mr. Baird's methods, admits of no manner of doubt. Those who deny it simply have not seen it."

With controversy raging around his system and achievements Baird was unrelenting in his tireless experiments to bring forward additional *proof* to confront the sceptics. Never once did he personally enter into the conflict by written or spoken word, although his feelings might quite conceivably have been bitter at the difficulties placed in his path when his outstanding achievements of the past three years might well have earned him sympathetic co-operation. His patience, no doubt trained by earlier trials, was inexhaustible, his fortitude and charity of mind something to marvel at. In the very few comments I heard from him in private discussions at this time sorrow rather than anger was clearly manifest. He had such unswerving

BAIRD IN 1929

Drawn by Edmund J. Sullivan, A.R.W.S., A.R.E.

[*Reproduced from "Everyman," with permission.*

faith that matters would right themselves that Baird simply refused to be depressed.

Early in 1929, when some die-hard critics were challenging Baird to demonstrate any improvement in his system, he gave the first exhibitions of whole stage scenes to visitors at the laboratory. We saw two boxers fighting on a stage about 15 feet by 10 feet, and on the small reception screen witnessed clearly the exchange of blows and quick movements of the combatants, and then a cyclist was seen to ride round the stage. The well-known play, *Box and Cox*, was performed on this small stage and transmitted in its entirety in an experimental broadcast after midnight. Baird also at this time succeeded in projecting his received images on to a larger screen, some four feet in diameter, thus permitting them to be viewed by greater numbers.

The visitors' book just then shows us how many very distinguished visitors called on Baird to gain first-hand impressions of his work, and there is no doubt that many of their opinions reached the ears of the Postmaster-General. It is to the credit of Sir William Mitchell Thompson that he came, with Viscount Wolmer, his assistant, to meet Baird and find out the truth for himself. He afterwards stated in Parliament that television was to be tested by broadcasting.

On 5th March 1929 the official test (I almost wrote "trial") of Baird's system took place through 2LO in the presence of Post Office officials, B.B.C officials, and a committee of Members of Parliament. Receivers were installed at Savoy Hill and at a room in the Secretary's Department, General Post Office, E.C.1, and among those televised on this now historic demonstration was Jack Buchanan, who cheerfully turned out for his old friend. The Postmaster-General's report which was issued on 27th March placed the official seal on Baird's system as "a noteworthy scientific achievement," and agreed to the use of a B.B.C. station for progressive experimental transmissions.

Negotiations began between the B.B.C. and the Baird interests, and it seemed that what had been a delicate situation was taking a happy turn. But just once more Baird was to know a lack in his own country of the vision and hearty co-operation which he had experienced in European countries. The B.B.C. offered but three transmission periods per week of fifteen minutes at 11 a.m., with no guarantee of continuity, and negotiations broke down. Following a visit to the Baird laboratories by Mr. Lees-Smith, the new Postmaster-General, the B.B.C. offered five half-hours a week for television transmissions.

Extract from

CHIEF BROADCAST EVENTS IN 1932.

(Issued by the British Broadcasting Corporation)

"From August 22 television programmes have been broadcast on Mondays, Tuesdays, Wednesdays and Fridays of each week from 11.0 to 11.30 p.m., sound being transmitted on 398.9 metres and vision on 261.3 metres.

The programmes, which have been remarkable for a variety of talent that has been seen and heard, included Mr and Mrs Mollison, an exhibition of art treasures opened by Lord Lee of Fareham, a display of exclusive fashions by a leading London modist, Ju Jitsu and fencing, ventriloquists, Carl Brisson, Erik Bertner, a performing seal, a selection of Christmas toys, a music hall programme reminiscent of the nineties, and Delysia.

The year culminated in a Boxing Day pantomime, Dick Whittington, the first television pantomime ever put on the air, complete with cat, property rats, sub-titles showing changes of scenes, drawings of mosques and minarets and of the Mansion House London".

THE B.B.C. AND BAIRD

The above is evidence of the cordial spirit of co-operation now evinced by the B.B.C. towards Baird television.

So ended a period which reflected but little credit in many quarters, but through which the sterling qualities of Baird's character and his unswerving faith in his own system carried him finally triumphant. Still, it is finished, and the pipe of peace has long been smoked. Let the episode be confined to the limbo of the past. Cordial co-operation is the order of to-day!

C H A P T E R T E N

HONOUR WHERE HONOUR IS DUE

CHAPTER TEN

HONOUR WHERE HONOUR IS DUE

ON Monday morning, 30th September 1929, Baird stood modestly in a corner of the studio in Long Acre and witnessed the inaugural broadcast of television carried out through the B.B.C. transmitter 2LO for half an hour. This Scotsman, whose fortitude had been proof against all difficulties and disappointments for five years, and who had conceived and brought into being a new era in communication, heard the following message from the Rt. Hon. William Graham, P.C., President of the Board of Trade, and member of the British Cabinet, read to the public:

"It was with great pleasure I received the invitation to speak and be seen on this occasion of the first public experimental broadcast of television, and I deeply regret that circumstances prevent me from being present. I look to this new applied science to encourage and provide a new industry, not only for Britain and the British Empire, but for the whole world. This new industry will provide employment for large numbers of our people and will prove the prestige of British creative energy.

In this first public broadcast we have a beginning which will be historic in the evolution not only of a science, but of an art which will encourage closer relations between communities at home and abroad and provide a new avenue for educational development."

Afterwards Baird was persuaded to appear before the transmitter and say just a few words.

These broadcasts were sent out from one transmitter only, as no second was available for a time, and sound and vision had to be sent alternately. From 31st March 1930, however, two wave-lengths were allotted and have been in use to this day, the sound being transmitted on one, and the vision on the other, for the benefit of those equipped with receiving apparatus. Mr. R. C. Sherriff was among those who made an appearance in the inaugural sight-and-sound programme and a "Televisor" was installed at 10 Downing Street to enable the Prime Minister and his household to enjoy the programme.

The Prime Minister had visited Mr. Baird at his laboratory earlier, to see television and noctovision, and was particularly impressed with the latter and warmly congratulated Baird. On 1st April Mr. MacDonald utilised his receiver to entertain a number of delegates to the London Naval Conference. Among the many mementoes which Baird has collected I saw a letter dated from Downing Street on 5th April 1930, which read:

DEAR MR. BAIRD,

I must thank you very warmly for the television instrument you have put into Downing Street. What a marvellous discovery you have made! When I look at the transmissions I feel that the most wonderful miracle is being done under my eye. I congratulate you most heartily and send you my sincerest hopes for your further success. You have put something in my room which will never let me forget how strange is the world—and how unknown. Again and again I thank you.

With kindest regards,

Yours very sincerely,

J. RAMSAY MACDONALD.

(*See page* 155.)

It was on 17th July 1929 that the Prince of Wales attended a dinner at the Caledonian Club, London, and Baird was present as a member of the club. Afterwards Baird was presented to His Royal Highness and gave a demonstration of television, which was transmitted to the club from the Long Acre studio. The Prince was greatly interested, and watched the performance and chatted to Baird for about half an hour.

Towards the end of 1929 Hastings decided to pay due tribute to Baird's early associations with, and notable achievements in, the town. So seldom do outstanding men of genius receive due recognition before they are too aged to appreciate it—or dead and buried—that it was refreshing indeed to learn that the town council had decided to erect a tablet on the wall of No. 8 Queen's Arcade, the address at which, as recorded earlier in this volume, Baird commenced his serious television research which led to partial success before removal to London.

On 7th November 1929 the bronze plaque, bearing the inscription quoted in an earlier chapter, was unveiled by the Mayor of Hastings, Councillor A. D. Thorpe, J.P., in the presence of Mr. Baird, officials of the Television Society, Members of the Council, and others. More mundane affairs prevented my attendance, but the proceedings were reported to me by friends present.

No speeches were made at the unveiling in the little passage-way of Queen's Arcade, but the party proceeded to the Council Chamber at the Town Hall. Here the Mayor read a letter of regret at inability to attend from Sir Ambrose Fleming, D.Sc.:

"I regret very much that another important engagement at the Institution of Electrical Engineers to-night prevents me from accepting the

5 April 1930

10 Downing Street.
Whitehall

Dear Mr Baird

I must thank you very warmly for the Television instrument you have put into Downing St.. What a marvellous discovery you have made! When I look at the transmissions I feel that the most wonderful miracle is being done under my eye. I congratulate you most heartily & send you my sincerest hopes for your further success. You have put something in my room which will never let me forget how strange is this world – and how unknown. Again & again I thank you.

With kindest regards

Yours very sincerely

J. Ramsay MacDonald

Facsimile of the Prime Minister's letter to Baird. (*See page* 153.)

kind invitation of the Mayor of Hastings to be present at the interesting ceremony of the unveiling of a plaque commemorating the historic and epoch-making work of Mr. Baird. This plaque will be a perpetual reminder that Mr. Baird was the first to effect practical television and to inaugurate a new departure in electrical technics which will have immense developments in present and future years."

"We are very proud in Hastings," said the Mayor in the course of a short speech, "to be associated with the great name of Baird. Hastings has many distinctions, but perhaps this one in the years to come will be one of its most famous, and we are sure Mr. Baird is proud to be associated with Hastings. He will never forget his scientific achievements here and the place where he worked.

"Mr. Baird," the Mayor continued, "like many famous Scotsmen, was a son of the Manse, and when he came down to Hastings he was a struggling but intelligent young Scotsman. Mr. Baird represented for them a man who had conquered many difficulties. He had struggled for years, worked hard, and had had to negotiate many fences in his efforts to develop television. Mr. Baird is only forty years of age, and we are looking forward to seeing him spared in health and strength to carry on his invention to very great lengths indeed and to be one of the most famous men in England."

Baird was given an ovation when rising to reply, and after thanking the Mayor and people of Hastings for the honour and the pleasure they had given him he went on to say: "When I arrived in Hastings in 1922 I came in search of health after a serious illness, and thought I would never be fit and well again—the doctor who sent me also thought the same, but in a very short time the exhilarating atmosphere of Hastings made me a changed man. While down here doing nothing I took up the study of television again. I had been interested in it since my youth, and when I took it up here with the aid of some apparatus I managed to get together I soon began to get shadowy images to appear on the television screen. In a little back room above what used to be an artificial flower shop in the Queen's Arcade, these first experiments were carried out, and although nothing very much was seen through these early machines it was sufficient to show that the right path was being followed. It is interesting, too, to note that the machines now used are, in principle, almost identical with that early apparatus. I need not go into technical details, but there are the same neon tubes, the same disc with its holes, and the same type of motor to drive the disc."

Dr. Clarence Tierney, the Chairman of the Television Society, who afterwards spoke, said it was surprising how few people could read history in the making. They should feel privileged at having been allowed to take part in the writing of a page of it that afternoon, for undoubtedly that event, simple as it might appear, was a page in history that, as the years went on, might become a very important one.

Baird's native country also honoured him, for on the occasion of the first public demonstrations of television in Scotland, which were given at Kelvin Hall, Glasgow, at the end of January 1930, he was awarded a medal specially struck for the occasion. Unfortunately an attack of influenza prevented his attending to receive this in public.

The Scottish Press were unanimous in their praise of his achievements as shown at these demonstrations, and the Rev. Mr. McLellan preached a sermon at Trinity Church on Sunday evening, 2nd February, before a congregation of more than a thousand, in which he took for his subject the work of John Logie Baird.

If my previous chapter reveals some of the criticism and lack of co-operation with which Baird was faced at times, this present one serves to show that there was also a happier side of the picture when his epochal work was duly recognised.

HASTINGS HONOURS BAIRD.

THE MAYOR OF HASTINGS & BAIRD PHOTOGRAPHED ON 7TH NOVEMBER, 1929, AT THE UNVEILING OF THE TABLET ERECTED BY THE TOWN OF HASTINGS TO COMMEMORATE BAIRD'S EARLY TELEVISION RESEARCH WORK THERE.

CHAPTER ELEVEN

FURTHER ACHIEVEMENTS

L

CHAPTER ELEVEN

FURTHER ACHIEVEMENTS

ONE of Baird's most significant achievements was the solution of the problem of synchronisation between transmitter and receiver. To the layman this does not appear so spectacular an advance as, say, daylight television or television in colours, yet the scientists knew that not until the problem of obtaining absolute synchronisation was solved could television attain definite commercial possibilities.

In America, and elsewhere, many attempts had been made to achieve the desired result, for television was quite definitely ruled out as a medium of home entertainment until a system of synchronisation could be developed which would be simple and inexpensive and not necessitate the use of a separate channel of communication.

Following months of most intense work, in absolute secrecy, Baird produced the first satisfactory solution of the difficult problem, and the first public demonstration of a self-synchronised television receiver by wire took place at the 1928

Radio Exhibition, while the first public wireless demonstration took place before the Postmaster-General at the official test of Baird's system in March 1929. The picture itself provided the synchronising impulses in the latter case through 2LO, speech was sent on a separate wave-length, and no separate signals were needed.

Another product of Baird's fertile brain was "Phonovision," whereby living scenes, whilst being transmitted, are recorded on wax records and stored up for future use. In television the scene before the transmitter is transformed into an undulating electrical current which is sent out either by wire or wireless. If one tunes in this transmission, the current can be heard on headphones, and so these "image sounds" can be played into a recording gramophone and permanently "bottled" like any other sounds. When required, these sounds are played with an electrical pick-up connected to a "Televisor" and the original scene is reproduced.

In August 1929 Baird gave the first public demonstrations of "Tele-Talkies," or the transmission of normal talking films by television. Some years earlier he had experimented in the transmission of silent films by television, but it was found to arouse but little interest; however, by using a talking film, greater interest was stimulated, and it was felt that here was a useful medium for occasional use in general television programmes.

Round about this time the inhabitants of the Dorking Valley had been mystified by reports of moving lights and signalling at night, and the explanation was forthcoming when Baird invited journalists and scientists to his house at Boxhill to witness the result of his efforts to raise "Noctovision" from a scientific curiosity into something of commercial value.

The apparatus he showed us was designed to enable ships at sea, in the thickest fog, to pick up the navigation lights of other vessels, or the rays of a lighthouse, and determine their relative bearings. A car was sent out at nightfall and we watched its lights as it moved along the main road in the valley below. At a distance of three or four miles it stopped and turned one headlight towards the house.

At a signal from Baird's house the headlight vanished in the darkness, the light having been obliterated by placing a sheet of ebonite in front of it as an artificial substitute for fog. This was now supposed to be the light of a vessel in a thick fog and in his garden Baird swung around his "Noctovisor" just as the navigator would on a vessel in fog. Suddenly the light of the obscured head-

Early in 1931 Baird showed yet another development, this time zone-television, which was intended for use in theatres and cinemas where several telephone lines would be available, as apart from home television. In this apparatus the scene was not scanned by a moving light spot, but was illuminated by ordinary flood-lighting, and those invited to witness demonstrations saw as many as eight full-length figures projected on the receiving screen. These scenes were made up of three sections transmitted side by side.

Invited to witness one of these zone-television tests, I called at the laboratory and viewed the illuminated stage, then on the transmitter I watched Herbert Strudwick, the Surrey and England professional, demonstrating cricket strokes before a wicket. Afterwards two young boxers gave a demonstration, and then we saw half a dozen people standing and seated round a table, the detail and clarity of the images being remarkable. On this occasion I took with me Mr. H. E. Cossins, a well-known radio experimenter who had not before visited Baird, and he was tremendously enthusiastic at what he saw and at the vast potentialities of the demonstration.

Reporting on these demonstrations the technical editor of *To-day's Cinema* wrote: "It is my firm belief that Baird has at last hit on the very method which will bring television into the cinemas. It is a bold statement, but I make it in all seriousness and when I saw yesterday's demonstration I could see, beyond the tiny screen shown to a visitor, a new revolution in our industry."

On 8th May 1931, for the first time in history, Baird gave a demonstration of the televising of street scenes in normal daylight. A van was drawn up in Long Acre and a revolving mirror drum picked up the scene which was transmitted by landline to watching Press representatives. In the *Daily Mail* for the following day we read: "A *Daily Mail* reporter looked into the television receiving machine in a room in Long Acre and saw the images of people passing to and fro in the street below. There was considerable variation in the quality of reception, due to varying degrees of cloud and sunshine, but the panorama of the street was there—small boys looking at the transmitting machine in the road, a white-coated seller of chocolates, and so on."

It was the achievements of Baird which made it possible for the *Daily Herald*, on 13th May 1931, to secure the world's first newspaper interview by television. Baird's apparatus was installed in No. 11 Downing Street and in the editor's room.

Towards the end of April 1932 Baird gave the first public demonstration in any country of television by ultra-short wave at Selfridge's Store. The wave-length used was 6·1 metres, and most promising results were seen at the demonstration. The great advantage of the development of these ultra-short wave transmissions was that television programmes could be put on the ether without interfering with the ordinary broadcasting from B.B.C. or foreign stations, and at the demonstration Baird told journalists that by the use of appropriate apparatus the ultra-short wave work was enabling a wealth of detail to be transmitted without flicker.

A month later yet another historic feat of television was made possible by Baird's apparatus, although he was not able to be present in person. The *Daily Mail* report on 20th May read: "Television has made a distinct advance, judging from a two-way demonstration to-day between the offices of the newspaper *Le Matin* and the Galeries Lafayette, the big Paris Stores. Using an ordinary telephone I was able not only to converse from the newspaper office with people in the Stores, but also to see them, and they could see me and talk to me.

"This is the first demonstration ever to have been given outside a laboratory of two-way tele-

THE NEW TELEVISION AT SELFRIDGE'S.

The policy of the House of Selfridge has always been to link up with any forward movement designed to advance human relationship, with improvements that will lead to a higher culture and a betterment of our social existence.

In no direction have we gained greater satisfaction than our association with television since its very inception, for just over seven years ago—in April, 1925—Mr. J. L. Baird gave his first demonstration of Television or "seeing by Wireless", as it was then called—in this Store.

The image then transmitted was of the simplest—a letter of the alphabet on a screen about the size of a postage stamp. The apparatus by which it was accomplished was of the crudest. A contemporary writer described Baird's apparatus as being "built out of odds and ends and lenses taken out of old cycle lamps, the framework an unimpressive erection of old sugar boxes and the electrical wiring a night-mare of improvisation."

From those inauspicious beginnings has grown the practical transmission of visual images by wireless.

In March, 1929, when Selfridge's was 2 LO. (many will call to mind the giant wireless masts on the roof) a demonstration was given to the B.B.C. and the Post Master General.

And since September, 1929, programmes transmitted from the B.B.C. station have been shown in the Store and have given pleasure to many thousands of visitors.

RAPID PROGRESS OF THE INVENTION.

In the early part of this year the first demonstration of Baird Television, on a screen so that the image could be seen by a roomful of people, on ultra short waves (6.1 metres) was given on the roof here. The Television Screen then used was only 12 inches by 4 inches. Today we are showing pictures on a screen 3 feet by 7 feet.

To many people Television, with its possibilities, presents a devastating outlook, for doubtless it will be extended to the telephone. On the other hand it will afford so many conveniences, that, as with most other modern inventions, we shall wonder how we got on without it in the past.

THE BIRTH OF A GIGANTIC INDUSTRY.

Both the studio, housing the transmitting apparatus and the screen receiver are situated at different sections of the Fourth Floor and the daily programme includes the Televising of well-known stage artistes, celebrities **and the general public**.

The images of the persons being transmitted from the studio are reflected on to photo-electric cells and the resulting variations in current from these cells are received by the Baird Screen "Televisor." Here they control a Baird grid cell placed in front of an arc lamp, the light from this arc lamp being varied by the Baird cell in accordance with the signals received. This light is then projected on to a revolving mirror drum and thence to the screen facing the audience.

Obviously, every big invention or development has a beginning and it is therefore necessary to realise that what is being seen is probably the birth of a gigantic industry, and the images which will be produced in the near future will, it is hoped, be equal in every way to that of the Modern Cinema.

Selfridge & Co. Ltd. *Oxford Street, London.*

Reproduction of a circular issued by Selfridge's, which appeared towards the end of 1932.

vision, the system used being the Baird, which in France will be known as the Baird-Nathan system. I understand that it is to be applied by the Galeries Lafayette between their establishments in Paris and Lyons. . . . The screen on which the face is reproduced measures about 10 inches by 5 inches. Among those who attended the demonstration was M. Louis Rollin, the French Minister of Commerce."

It requires little effort to remember Baird's crowning success at the 1932 Derby when the scenes in the race were broadcast through B.B.C. stations, and also transmitted by landline to the audience of a London cinema, where television was figuring in the normal programme throughout the week.

The caravan was once again sent down to the course and every step of the preparatory work was personally checked by Baird himself. He worked tremendously hard for the two or three days before the race and at the time of the transmission was in charge behind the big screen at the cinema. Once again I will quote from the *Daily Herald* (2nd June 1932):

"With five thousand people in the Metropole Cinema, Victoria, S.W., fifteen miles from Epsom, I watched the finish of the Derby, while thousands on the Downs saw nothing of yesterday's great race.

It was the most thrilling demonstration of the possibilities of television yet witnessed. It made history. So distinct was the scene shown on a screen, nine feet by seven feet, that the watchers forgot the race in face of the miracle that brought it before their eyes. Many of us can remember the thrill of those first 'moving pictures.' They flickered and spluttered, but out of the haze we saw men move about. Television, as we saw it yesterday, is in that stage, although the flicker is not so bad as those early films.

"We saw the horses quite distinctly as they came up the straight, April the Fifth ahead, with Dastur and Miracle close behind. We could discern the black-and-white figures of the crouching jockeys and distinguish them by the shapes of the colours they wore! As we sat in that darkened theatre distance was annihilated. We were the first people in the world to see such a spectacle on a cinema screen. 'Marvellous! Marvellous!' shouted men and women around me.

"While the excitement still raged on the Downs we were cheering Tom Walls' success, and then we came back to earth. Mr. J. L. Baird, the inventor who made the marvel possible, stepped on to the stage and received a bigger cheer than April the Fifth. He was too thrilled to say a word."

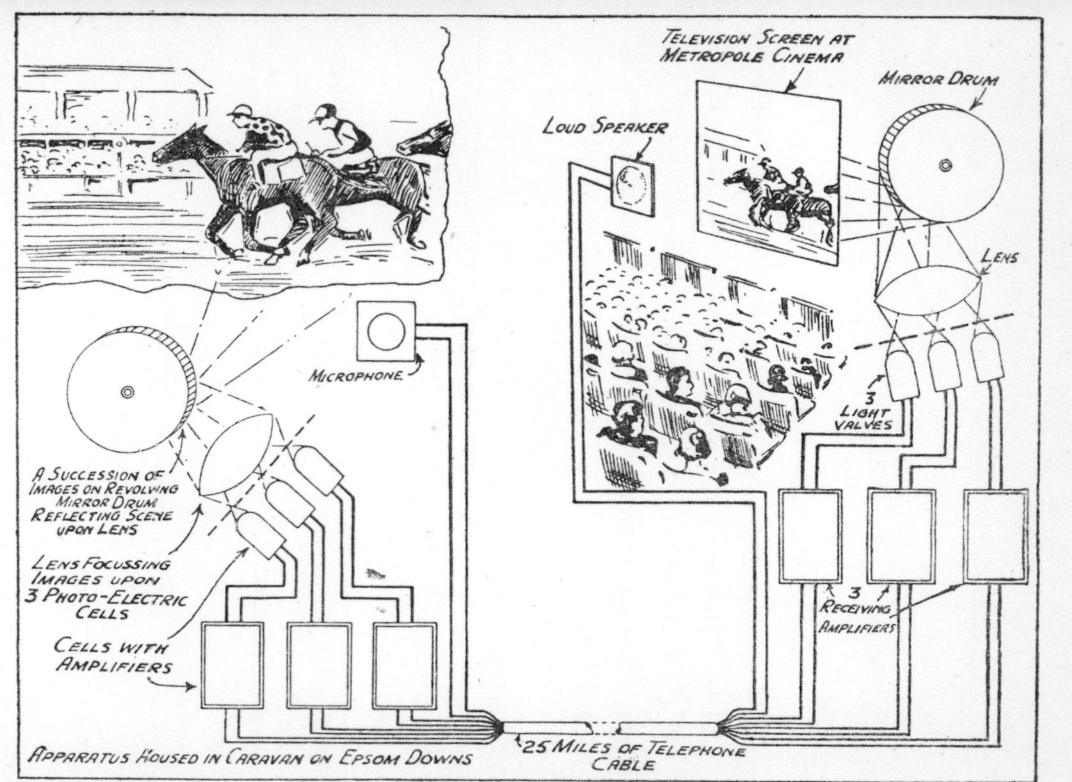

A Further Advance in Television

A pictorial diagram showing the general arrangement of the apparatus by which scenes at the 1932 Derby were transmitted from the race-course to a cinema screen in London.

[*Reproduced from the magazine "Television" by permission.*

CHAPTER TWELVE

IN THE U.S.A.

covering from a sudden attack of influenza, the ceremony was a private one. When the fact became known congratulations poured in from many countries.

Mrs. Baird was born at Johannesburg, South Africa, on 13th March 1907, and is a niece of Sir Henry Albu, the chief of the great South African gold-mining syndicate. She had a natural talent for music and began studying the pianoforte at the age of six. When eighteen years of age she came to London, and in eighteen months had obtained both the L.R.A.M. and the A.R.C.M. degrees. Since then she has climbed high in her profession, and her recitals at the Grotrian Hall brought her name into prominence.

Having been invited to Mr. and Mrs. Baird's delightful Boxhill home shortly after their return from America, I can give personal testimony as to Mrs. Baird's charm as a hostess.

Shortly after arrival in the States Baird found the interest in his system so keen that he cabled for the caravan, which was used for the Derby broadcast, to be sent out. Soon he was able to announce an agreement with the Knickerbocker Broadcasting Corporation of New York to put his system of television on the air daily in New York, subject to the granting of a licence by the Federal Radio Commission.

This Corporation thoroughly investigated the Baird and all rival systems and chose the Baird system in preference to any American one for broadcasting from Station W.M.C.A., one of the largest broadcasting stations in America. However, on 18th March 1932, the Federal Radio Commission refused to grant the necessary licence on the grounds that no foreign company must be permitted to broadcast, either directly or indirectly, in the United States.

On Sunday evening, 18th October 1931, Baird was invited to broadcast a talk from stations W.M.C.A. and W.P.C.H., New York, and here is the text of the speech he gave on that occasion:

"Ladies and Gentlemen,

"It is a very great pleasure and privilege to address you by the invitation of Station W.M.C.A., which has asked me to give you a short talk on my impressions of New York, and to say a few words about my work on television. Before doing so, however, may I pause for a very brief moment to say that in the death early this morning of Thomas A. Edison, the world at large lost a great benefactor and one of the greatest pioneers of electrical science. Almost every branch of scientific research was enriched by his contributions. In many parts of

add to the word description of the fight by transmitting scenes of the actual fight itself. In addition, arrangements are being made for broadcasting outstanding theatrical events, such as opening nights of Broadway productions. This will be done with apparatus similar to that which we are using in England for broadcasting scenes such as the Derby horse-race as we did in June last.

"I know you are all very much interested in what is being done in Europe in television, and perhaps you would like to hear some of my own early personal experiences." (Here Baird gave a brief and modest résumé of his achievements from 1925 to date.)

"I will conclude now by saying that television is only in its infancy and big developments are pending. The television images which have been seen by the general public are no criterion of what has been achieved in the laboratories. Our work now is to simplify and cheapen our present laboratory apparatus, so that it can be made available to the man in the street. The problem of television is solved. What remains to be done is entirely a matter of technical and commercial development.

"Throughout the world the highest scientific thought is being devoted to television. Vast strides have been made, and will be made, in this new art. I myself look forward to seeing, in the not far distant future, television theatres supersede the talkies, and the home 'Televisor' become as common as the home radio is to-day."

BAIRD WITH THE AUTHOR TO-DAY.

BAIRD DEMONSTRATING TO THE AUTHOR IN 1933 A MODERN COMMERCIAL "TELEVISOR" OF THE TYPE IN REGULAR USE IN THOUSANDS OF HOMES FOR RECEPTION OF THE B.B.C. TELEVISED PROGRAMMES.

CHAPTER THIRTEEN

BAIRD TO-DAY

TO-DAY John Logie Baird can look back over a career with strange contrasts of discouraging hardships and crowning successes—but he does not look back. He looks ever forward. He remains a modest explorer constantly seeking something in realms beyond.

To-day he finds the marvels conjured by his brilliant inventive faculties slowly but surely opening up a new era of world communication, and revolutionising the world in which we live. In England, programmes made possible by his achievements are broadcast almost daily, and all who wish may equip themselves with the necessary receiver—every one bearing Baird's facsimile signature—*and see!* In Germany, France, and Italy his system takes premier place in development, while in the U.S.A. it was chosen for broadcasting, but owing to the attitude of the Federal Radio Commission this was not possible.

He is not by any means content to rest upon his hard-won laurels, for to this day he remains a tireless

dinner perfectly served, from the cocktails to the coffee.

Thus I have had opportunities of studying his character from those early days when his name was becoming known to comparatively few, until to-day when it is a household word in many lands. On each occasion I found the same innate courtesy, kindly sympathy, simplicity of character, and human understanding.

This television with which Baird's name is indissolubly linked adds another to the long list of notable conquests of science. Within memory of living man great advances have been made in so many fields. The telephone was seen as but an interesting toy, the phonograph was novel rather than useful, the motor car was just a noisy and odorous nuisance, while aviation and wireless telephony were left to the imaginative novelists.

Yet to-day the world could not do without the convenience of the telephone, the gramophone reproduces music with a purity beyond reproach, the motor car is silent, speedy, and luxurious, while the aeroplane is a perfectly normal means of transit and the loud-speaker opens up many avenues of interest, amusement, and education.

Just as so many other inventions in the past have been improved and refined to meet more fully the needs of mankind, so television will be developed and will play an ever-increasing part in our daily lives as fresh practical applications for its increasing possibilities are found.

The complete influence of television upon man's life in the future is difficult to visualise, but it may be said that all the vast potentialities of the art were released as the result of the brilliant success of the young Scottish engineer whose romantic life-story has been told in these pages.

The *New York Times* of 13th September 1931 paid due tribute to the genius of Baird by including in their list of outstanding scientific achievements of the past eighty years his demonstration of television in 1926, and there is no doubt that this first demonstration of true television to the world stands for all time as a British triumph on the pages of scientific history.

To conclude, I cannot, perhaps, do better than to quote from a magazine article written by Mr. Louis Byrne, a well-known Fleet Street journalist:

"Let it be said, therefore, at this point, that in giving us reproduced light rays with their varying frequency and intensity in the form of readily recognisable images, Mr. Baird must go down in the history book of science as an inventor of the greatest calibre, to whom future generations will

THE NEW YORK TIMES, SUNDAY, SEPTEMBER 13, 1931.

THE OUTSTANDING INVENTIONS OF THE PAST EIGHTY YEARS

The prophecies on this page, describing the world as it may be eighty years hence, assume added significance in the light of man's record of invention in the past eighty—since the day when the first issue of The New York Times appeared. What follows is a compilation of the outstanding inventions since 1851:

1852—Elisha Gray Otis invents the elevator with automatic braking mechanism, later developed for office and building use.

1853—Cintl, an Austrian technician, shows how two messages can be sent over a single telegraph wire (duplex telegraphy).

1854—Henry D. Stone and Frederick W. Howe perfect the turret lathe so that a number of tools may cut metal mechanically. The general idea of the turret lathe goes back to Stephen Fitch (1845).

1855—Robert Wilhelm von Bunsen invents the burner now used in every gas stove.

1856—Sir Henry Bessemer devises the process for making Bessemer steel.

1860—Dr. Antonio Pacinotti conceives the first continuous-current dynamo but does nothing with it. It is independently re-invented by the Belgian Z. T. Gramme (1870-1872).

1861—Coleman Sellers of Philadelphia patents and demonstrates the first motion-picture machine of the modern type. Edison brings out the commercial apparatus in 1893.

Wilhelm Siemens invents the regenerative furnace. This, in the hands of two Frenchmen, Pierre and Emile Martin, is applied in making open-hearth steel (1864).

1865—William Bullock of Philadelphia builds the first press to print from a continuous roll or web of paper.

1867—Christopher L. Sholes invents the modern typewriter. Perfected in 1873.

1868—George Westinghouse demonstrates his airbrake.

1869—J. H. Greathead designs the modern shield used in tunneling under water.

1870—Sir William Siemens invents the electric furnace for melting iron and steel.

1871—Charles Goodyear Jr. invents the welt-shoemaking machine.

1874—Thomas A. Edison devises the quadruplex telegraph, which sends four messages over a single wire.

Sir William Thompson (afterward Lord Kelvin) devises the syphon recorder, which becomes indispensable in writing down cable messages.

1876—Alexander Graham Bell and Elisha Gray independently invent the telephone.

Dr. N. A. Otto of Cologne, Germany, invents the four-cycle internal-combustion engine now generally used in automobiles.

1877—Thomas A. Edison demonstrates his phonograph.

1879—Thomas A. Edison produces the first practical incandescent electric lamp.

1884—Sir Charles A. Parsons receives the first patent for his steam turbine

The modern trolley car appears. Van Depoele invents the trolley wheel and Frank L. Sprague the multiple-unit system of control.

Gottlieb Daimler brings out the light compact gasoline engine of today and in 1885 drives a bicycle with it. Thus the automobile begins. Carl Benz of Karlsruhe is simultaneously working on the automobile problem and turns out his first gasoline vehicle.

1886—Ottmar Mergenthaler perfects his linotype machine.

Hall produces aluminum, by an electrical process which eventually becomes commercial.

1887—Tolbert Lanston patents the monotype.

The Rev. Hannibal Goodwin patents the celluloid film. George Eastman independently works out the same principle.

The induction motor of Nikola Tesla appears.

1888—John Boyd Dunlop reinvents the double-tube pneumatic tire, the original invention of Robert W. Thompson (1845) having been forgotten.

1890—Dr. Carl Auer von Welsbach produces his montle burner.

1893—Rudolf Diesel publishes a description of his proposed engine. The first specimens are exhibited in 1898 at Munich.

1896—Guglielmo Marconi patents the first high frequency system of wireless telegraphy.

1899—Francis Elmore first actually uses the oil-flotation process for separating ores from waste. The germs of ore flotation are also found in a patent granted to Carry J. Everson of Denver, Col. (1886).

1900—Héroult devises his furnace for producing steel electrically.

1901—Frederick W. Taylor and Maunsel White develop the modern high-speed alloy steels which have made the cheap production of automobiles and other machines possible.

1902—Professor Arthur Korn of Germany makes the first long-distance experiment in transmitting photographs by wire.

1903—The Wright brothers produce a motor-driven airplane and fly it successfully at Kitty Hawk, N. C.

Valdemar Poulsen and Reginald Fessenden independently devise successful experimental radio telephones.

1906—Dr. Lee De Forest invents the vacuum tube now indispensable in all electrical communication

1926—J. L. Baird sends recognizable television images over a wire.

A Tribute to Baird

The *New York Times* of 13th September 1931 included him in their list of outstanding inventions of the past eighty years. (See entry for 1926.)

not stint either praise or credit for the invention of, and the making practicable of, the modern development which we speak of to-day as television, or the ability to see over distance or through space electrically."

Rich as are the records of modern science in men who have triumphed over great obstacles, the story of John Logie Baird need fear comparison with none.

CHAPTER FOURTEEN

THIS TELEVISION

CHAPTER FOURTEEN

THIS TELEVISION

THROUGHOUT the life-story of John Logie Baird I have purposely avoided entering into technicalities regarding his apparatus and many developments. This book is not the correct place for these, and I can advise those interested in the technical aspect to read *Television To-day and To-morrow*, by Moseley and Chapple (Pitman), or *Practical Television*, by Larner (Benn), and the monthly magazine *Television*.

At the same time it is felt that a brief outline of certain broad principles of this television with which Baird's name is linked would assist in the full appreciation of his work and make the narrative quite complete. Rather than interrupt the story earlier in the volume with explanations it was thought better to collect these as a separate and concluding chapter of the volume.

The word "television" itself is a hybrid, being derived from the Greek *tele*, "at a distance," and the Latin verb *video*, "I see," and so it is quite literally seeing at a distance. It is popularly referred to as "seeing by wireless," but that description is not accurate, for it is really seeing by telegraphy, either with or without wires between the transmitter and the receiving point. Television is reproduction of sight quite irrespective of intervening barriers, for it is the instantaneous transmission of the image of living or inanimate objects, persons or scenes with all gradations of light, shade, and detail, so that it is seen on the receiving screen just as they would appear to the eye of an observer on the spot. At present natural colouring is only to be seen in laboratory experiments.

Television does not, of course, assist us in any way to violate privacy unawares, for at the receiver one gets vision only of that which is within focus of the "electric eye" at the transmitting end. The still photographs which are sent at comparatively slow speeds by wire and wireless to the papers are transmitted by photo-telegraphy, and this must not be confused with the instantaneous reproduction of sight which television gives.

With the number of broadcast listeners steadily growing in every country, it may be quite safely asserted that the reception of speech over great distances is a commonplace achievement inspiring no awe, and yet, although for some time television has been transmitted regularly in Britain and abroad, the very idea of *seeing* over the same distances is still a source of complete wonder to many people. A brief comparison of the principles involved in either case will serve to show that the processes are somewhat akin and the one really no more or less strange than the other.

Picture a broadcast artiste before the microphone in a studio. She sings, and the sound waves of her voice impinge on the microphone, which converts them into a fluctuating electrical current which alters in exact unison with her voice; these minute variations are amplified and superimposed upon the high-frequency carrier wave of the station and radiated into space. These electro-magnetic waves ("wireless waves") produce minute voltages in the aerial circuit of your set, if it is tuned to the particular station, and these, after being amplified and rectified by the set, are passed to the loud speaker, which converts the varying current into sound waves once more, and so we hear the artiste's song. Thus in telephony sound is turned into an electrical current, sent over a distance as electrical vibrations (either by wireless or wire), and the electrical vibrations are turned back into sound at the receiving end.

With television much the same process is gone through. Assuming the same artiste appeared in a programme which was being televised, she would stand before the transmitting apparatus and the special lighting of her features would be reflected back upon sensitive photo-electric cells, while these cells convert the light into current variations. This varying current is then transmitted through space just as in the analogous case in the previous paragraph. When broadcasting the voice no actual sound is transmitted, and in television no actual sight is transmitted; in either case it is an electrical replica which is sent out. At the receiving end the television receiver handles the amplified incoming electrical fluctuations; these vary a light source, and thus current variations are turned back into light variations, while associated apparatus recreates the image of the artiste's features before your eyes. Thus in television the photo-electric cells replace the microphone of telephony transmission, while the special lamp and associated apparatus in the recciver replace the loud speaker in the general scheme of things.

Since moving to the palatial headquarters at Broadcasting House, Portland Place, London, the television transmissions which are produced and radiated by the British Broadcasting Corporation, utilising the Baird system, have come from Studio BB, the Dance Band Studio. The walls of this room are covered with drab boarding with bright blue joints, while the floor is black-and-white check. Here the televised artistes perform in their special make-up, dead white face, blue lips, and blue-shaded eyes.

The very varied items included in the excellent television transmissions from this studio are divided into three groups—close-up, semi-extended, and fully-extended views.

Let us watch a close-up turn, say a comedian, in this studio before the Baird spotlight transmitter. A powerful beam of light is mechanically broken up into a rapidly moving spot, this being done by projecting it on to a drum revolving 750 times a second, around the outer edge of which thirty small mirrors are set, each at a slightly different angle to its predecessor. The light striking the first moving mirror is reflected as a tiny area of illumination which runs up the head and shoulders of the comedian, creating a narrow strip of light; then the next mirror reflects a second strip of light in the same way, but just to the left of the original strip, and so on until the features have been scanned by thirty strips of light side by side, each strip just touching the neighbouring ones. Although only a tiny area of light is in this way thrown on the features at any one instant, the whole process of building up thirty strips of light is carried out $12\frac{1}{2}$ times per second, and to an onlooker it would appear that the comedian's features were completely illuminated.

A rapidly varying amount of light or shade is reflected back from the swift-moving spot of light as it passes over the comedian's head and shoulders, this depending upon the portion of the features scanned. Thus, as the spot traverses the forehead, a considerable amount of light is thrown back, whereas when it is passing over dark hair or eyebrows very little light is reflected. This varying *reflected* light falls upon the bank of photo-electric cells which form the "television eye" and exactly corresponding current variations are produced in the cell circuit. This varying electrical current is amplified and then radiated from the transmitting aerial of the B.B.C. station.

Two B.B.C. stations are employed in connection with the television transmissions, of course, the speech picked up by the microphone being transmitted in the usual way via one, and the vision picked up by the "electric eye" being transmitted on the other wave-length. When the two transmissions are received on two radio sets, one tuned to each station, the loud speaker attached to one gives the voice of the comedian, while the "Televisor" attached to the other set reproduces his features and motions perfectly synchronised with the speech.

If you tune in the vision signals of a television programme on a radio set with loud speaker attached, you would "hear the face" as a rapid high-pitched "me-me-me-me," for it is so that the loud speaker translates the varying electrical impulses by means of which the living images are carried between the television transmitter and receiver.

Having shown how the features of this comedian in the studio have been scanned by the "television eye" and an electrical replica radiated into space, the next explanation required is of the process whereby the signals are reconverted in the home into a living, moving miniature of the head and shoulders of the artist.

The form of commercial "Televisor" in popular use during 1932 and 1933 is seen in the photograph facing page 192. This employs a flat plate neon lamp whose large electrode glows brightly or darkly according to the varying signal strength passed to it by the valve receiving set. Thus the varying intensity of the light of the flickering neon lamp is reproducing exactly the variations of reflected light which fell upon the photo-electric cells in the studio. It now remains to form a picture by spreading this varying light over the viewing area, just as an artist builds up a complete picture by many brush touches.

To achieve this a disc bearing thirty holes in staggered formation turns at 750 revolutions a second before the neon lamp. The first hole allows a point of light to pass and draws a strip of varying light up the viewing area, the next hole then draws a strip alongside, and so on until the features which were broken up into thirty strips by the revolving mirrors at the transmitter are built up again by the reassembly of thirty light strips at the receiver, and the living head and shoulders of the comedian can be watched.

It is, of course, essential for the mirror drum at the transmitter and the disc at the receiver to revolve at precisely the same speed and to be exactly in step; that is to say, as the first mirror explores the first strip in the studio the first hole in the disc must simultaneously paint the same first varying strip of light at the receiver; and in Baird's process this is achieved in a most satisfactory manner by quite automatic synchronism.

In a newer receiver which Baird has more recently developed, instead of the neon lamp and revolving disc of the former model there is a projection lamp whose beam of light is modulated (by being passed through a pair of Nicol prisms and a Baird grid cell), and a miniature revolving drum bearing thirty mirrors which throws a varying light point on to a translucent screen. On this more compact model the images are brighter, can be viewed by a roomful of people, and are shown in clear black-and-white instead of the rather reddish images shown in the neon lamp receiver.

The reassembly of the image strips on the home receiver gives a complete living, moving picture, for as 12½ complete picture explorations are carried out every second, the eye has no opportunity of dwelling on the mechanics of the proceeding. Owing to the rapidity of the process and the well-known lag or persistence of vision the whole image appears simultaneously and, just as in the cinema, we see one moving and continuous reproduction. A simple test of this "time lag" of the eye is to whirl a lighted cigarette rapidly; although your brain assures you that it is a moving point the eye sees it as a ring of fire. Without this lag of the eye television in its true sense would be impossible.

INDEX

J. AND J. GRAY, PRINTERS, EDINBURGH—1933

67/12 C.

67/172